40 Days to

Real

LOVE

and Happiness in Your Marriage

A Companion Workbook for Real Love in Marriage

GREG BAER, M.D.

BLUE RIDGE PRESS

40 Days to Real Love ® *and Happiness in Your Marriage*
Copyright © 2008 by Greg Baer, M.D.

First Edition

Baer, Greg
    40 Days to Real Love and Happiness in Your Marriage
    ISBN 978-1-892319-31-9
    1. Relationships 2. Self-help 3. Psychology
Published by Blue Ridge Press PO Box 3075 Rome, GA 30164
    877-633-3568

Also by Greg Baer, M.D.—
Published by Gotham Books, a division of Penguin USA Group:
Real Love ® — The Truth About Finding Unconditional Love and Fulfilling Relationships
Real Love ® *in Marriage* — The Truth About Finding Genuine Happiness Now and Forever

Published by Blue Ridge Press:
Real Love ® — The Truth About Finding Unconditional Love and Fulfilling Relationships, Unabridged Audio Book — Seven 60 minute CDs
The Real Love ® *Companion* — Taking Steps Toward a Loving and Happy Life
Real Love ® *in Dating* — The Truth About Finding the Perfect Partner — Book and Unabridged Audio Book
Real Love ® *in Marriage* — Unabridged Audio Book, Blue Ridge Press
Real Love ® *in Parenting* — The Truth About Raising Happy and Responsible Children — Book and Unabridged Audio Book
Real Love ® *in the Workplace* - Eight Principles for Consistently Effective Leadership in Business
Real Love ® *and Freedom for the Soul* - Eliminating the Chains of Victimhood
The Truth About Love and Lies — Three 60 minute CDs
The Essentials of Real Love ® — Six DVDs, or Six CDs
The Essentials of Real Love ® *Workbook* for DVDs or CDs
The Essentials of Real Love ® *Bible Workbook* for DVDs or CDs
Real Love ® *for Wise Men and Women* - The Truth About Sharing Real Love

Printed in the United States
10 9 8 7 6 5 4 3 2 1

INTRODUCTION AND INSTRUCTIONS

The book *Real Love in Marriage* contains the principles that have enabled uncounted thousands of people across the globe to create and maintain richly rewarding marriages. It has been demonstrated, however, that in order to actually apply these principles many people require more than the simple presentation of them in written form. For the purpose of facilitating this learning, my associates and I have offered a variety of educational opportunities: video coaching segments, radio shows, live video chats, and more online at www. RealLove.com; teleconference calls; professional Real Love coaches; live seminars; and so on. In order to provide yet another way for people to practically apply the principles found in *Real Love in Marriage*, I am suggesting the daily program outlined in this book, *40 Days to Real Love and Happiness in Your Marriage*.

40 Days is an opportunity for you—as well as a direct challenge to you—to make a commitment to live the principles of *Real Love in Marriage* as you read them. There is no genuine learning until there is a change in behavior. Moreover, there is no truly useful learning until people are happier. As Aristotle said, "Happiness is the meaning and the purpose of life, the whole aim and end of human existence." The world is filled with people who are characterized as "smart" and "knowledgeable" but who are nonetheless confused, personally miserable, and unhappy in their relationships. Of what use, then, is all their intelligence and knowledge? Truly productive learning—that which leads to happiness—is the purpose of *40 Days*.

40 Days is designed to accompany the Gotham Books edition of *Real Love in Marriage* and will make frequent references to the page numbers found therein. If you have an older, Blue Ridge Press edition, of *Real Love in Marriage*, you'll need to acquire a copy of the Gotham Books version.

40 Days With Your Partner

Let us assume that you and your partner are both committed to working through the 40 days together. (If not, don't be the least bit discouraged. In a moment we'll be discussing how to proceed quite effectively on your own.) In that case, some simple procedural guidelines may be helpful:

- Each of you will need your own copy of *40 Days*, because you'll be making extensive notes of your own in the exercises in the book.
- Schedule a firm time each day when the two of you will meet to read and talk. In the business world, for example, almost everything happens as a result of scheduled meetings, where planning and discussion occurs. It is astonishing that we then expect families to succeed without such scheduled meetings. With hectic schedules, it's understandable that many couples can't make the same time available for every day of the week. In that case, at each meeting you might consider setting the time for the next day's meeting. But then hold that time inviolable, as you would any important business meeting.
- Set aside thirty minutes for your meeting. You may not use it all, but this will allow time for reading in *Real Love in Marriage* and for the exercises in *40 Days*. I suggest reading both books out loud to each other, only because we've discovered that this can become an intimate experience. If one of you is a more effective reader aloud, let that person do the reading. You'll figure out what works best for you. If you're having a difficult time finding thirty minutes for this meeting, *reprioritize your life*. There is nothing more important than creating a powerful foundation of love in your marriage. It will reward you an hundredfold—in personal happiness, in joy for your children, in productivity in your job, in your health, and in other areas.

Be flexible. You may discover, for example, that the reading of the book *Real Love in Marriage* may occupy more of your meeting time than you'd like—it takes about two minutes per page to read aloud—and you'd like to use more of the time in your meeting for discussion. In that case, you might agree to separately read the assigned pages of the book before you arrive at the meeting.

On some days, you may not be able to complete all the assignments given. Again, be flexible, and do what you can.

40 Days Without Your Partner

It would be ideal if both partners in a marriage or long-term committed relationship could work through *40 Days to Real Love and Happiness in Your Marriage* together, but how often do we get to struggle through life's trials in ideal circumstances? No, flat tires often arrive in the dark and in the rain. We get sick while we have jobs and children to take care of. And so it is that in a great many cases where one partner is eager to work on the marriage, the other partner is simply too resistant, withdrawn, angry, afraid, or otherwise unable to cooperate. If you are a willing partner in such a marriage, *do not wait* for your partner's cooperation before you begin to work through this book.

I cannot count the times I have seen a marriage revolutionized by the effect of the love of *one partner*, so if your partner isn't ready to read *Real Love in Marriage* or to make the commitment of the *40 Days*, experience the 40 days of transformation yourself. As you complete the exercises in this book, if you do them with an open heart, *you* will still become a more loving person and a more loving partner.

In most cases—the overwhelming majority of relationships, actually—one partner is dramatically affected by an increase in love from the other. Can you imagine that your partner doesn't want to feel loved unconditionally? As you complete this book, you'll learn how you can better find that love, which is the single element your relationship needs most, and you'll learn how to share it with him or her. In short, it doesn't matter if your partner is ready for this book or for *Real Love in Marriage*. It only matters whether *you* are willing to make the commitment to be a more loving human being. If you are, you can't lose. No matter what happens, you will become more loving and happier, and it's highly likely that you will have a profound impact on your partner.

If you are completing this book by yourself, you'll notice that on most of the 40 Days, there will be an assignment to talk to your spouse or to share what you have written with your spouse—either the same day or on the next day. On those occasions—for the sake of brevity—I will not be providing separate instructions for those of you who are working on this book without your partners. Instead, when you "solo students" come across directions to share an assignment with your partner, I suggest that you make one of the following choices:

- Simply omit that assignment to share with your partner.
- Carry out the assignment, but perform it as a kind of play in your mind, where you play both the part of yourself and that of your partner. You've been around your partner enough that you know pretty well what he or she will say in most interactions.
- Even though your partner isn't working through the book with you, carefully make the choice to fulfill this particular assignment with him or her. In some cases, you'll discover that your partner will be quite willing to do this. If your spouse is quite resistant to discussion of any particular principle or assignment, don't force his or her cooperation, which will not lead to feelings of unconditional love. In each instance, always remember that just because you're ready to talk about a subject does *not* mean that he or she is ready to hear what you wish to say. Further, if you begin to share something with your partner, and it becomes obvious that he or she is clearly not ready to listen—he or she becomes angry or withdrawn, for example— you can quickly terminate the conversation.

The Help of Friends

Some of the assignments in *40 Days* involve discussions with a friend of your choice. The more you share your growth with others, the more profound it will become. We need the love and support of each other. I also recognize how difficult this assignment will be for some, and for that reason the concept of sharing our lives with others is explained on pages 65-80 in *Real Love in Marriage*. When it comes to the assignments regarding sharing with friends, do what you can.

Commitment

Generally, you'll see the most powerful results in your own life and in your relationship if you complete the program of the book in forty consecutive days. Positive transformation is much more likely when we engage in the use of effective tools intensively and regularly. We all know, for example, that if we want to get into good physical shape, it's not enough to work out vigorously once a month. The inactive time between workouts allows our bodies to return to their former, flabby condition.

(The same is true with conditioning our minds and hearts.) The more intensively and regularly that we engage in retraining the way we think and feel, the more effectively we will experience the transformations we seek in our individual lives and in our relationships. But let's not become rigid about any program, especially one that focuses on love. If you skip a day or days in the workbook here and there, don't get excited. Just continue reading from the place you last read. If you skip more than three or four days, you might consider backtracking a day or more in the book, to remind you of what you last learned.

DAY ONE:

The Power of Real Love

First Assignment

In the meeting, read from the book *Real Love in Marriage*:
Begin   Page 1, Title: The Great Secret
End   Page 9, Title: What We Use Without Enough Real Love

(Complete the following assignments outside the meeting.)

Second Assignment

Actually do the meditation found on pages 6-7. Have a friend read to you from the top of page 6 (beginning with the words, "Imagine that you're having a difficult day . . .") to the top of page 7 (ending with the words, " . . . and you know they mean what they say.") Or you could read the words into some kind of recording device—which are available everywhere these days—and then listen to yourself read the meditation. Read slowly and gently.

In the following space describe how it felt to be unconditionally accepted by these people. While you were with them, did you feel any inclination at all to be angry at them—or to lie to them or withdraw from them?

could Not do it, No One loves me. Try

Third Assignment

Now, take another step. *While* you were with these people, did you feel any inclination to be angry at *anyone else*—at any of the people you know in real life? Were you irritated about any of the things that tend to go wrong around you—the dysfunctional computer or the car in the shop or the lawn that hasn't been mowed? While you were with these loving people, did you notice a change in your negative feelings toward everyone? *Including your partner?*

How would that Feel.

If you did:

- You're in a majority that includes almost everyone on the planet, because unconditional love—Real Love—really is what we all want more than anything else. When we have enough of it, we're happy. When we don't, we're not, and if we're unhappy in any given moment, we are reacting *not* to what someone is doing to us in that moment but to an accumulation of pain— a *lifetime* of pain—that results from not feeling sufficiently loved.
- You just learned something of incredible importance: Your partner is not the cause of how you feel and behave.

Fourth Assignment

In the following space describe a recent interaction with your partner where you did blame him or her for how you felt—angry, withdrawn, victimized, frustrated, whatever—as Mark did on pages 1-2.

Az TRip. Felt Not Loved but accused. Not part of the House Hunt. Abe + Annette - No Tour - Evezy thing I Liked - Was No fRom Annette. Just Save up.

Fifth Assignment

Carefully consider the definitions of Real Love and conditional love on pages 4-5 and 8-9. Remember that in Real Love there is no disappointment and anger. Many of us are so accustomed to disappointment and anger that we can't imagine the absence of these conditions, and then it's understandable that we also can't imagine a love that isn't affected by these poisons. But such a love does exist, and without that love a healthy marriage is simply impossible. With all this in mind, use the following space to answer each of the following numbered questions:

1. Is it possible that I was raised in an environment that was less than unconditionally loving? *Yes*
2. Is it possible that because I did not receive sufficient Real Love from childhood to the present time, that I have become unable to contribute the Real Love that is indispensable to a healthy marriage? *Yes*
3. Is it possible that I demonstrate the disappointment and anger that would make it impossible for my partner to feel loved unconditionally? *Yes*
4. In view of the above—*my* inability to be loving—is it possible that I have been inappropriately blaming my partner for my negative feelings and behaviors on quite a number of occasions, like the case I described in the Fourth Assignment above? *Yes*
5. If the above is the case, is it possible that I could learn to bring Real Love into my marriage and literally transform it? *Yes*
6. Am I willing to at least begin to take the steps to do that?
   I am willing To Take the steps To do that.

You'll be sharing this assignment with your partner tomorrow, on Day Two.

Sixth Assignment

Share the results of your Fourth and Fifth Assignments with a friend and use the following space to record your experience with that. Did you feel more accepted and loved by your friend as you shared the truth about yourself? Did he or she offer any suggestions that might prove useful as you share this assignment with your partner tomorrow?

Sharing assignments with a loving friend before sharing them with your partner can often be effective. A friend may give you,some of the unconditional love that you can then bring to the interaction with your partner. Or your friend may offer feedback that will help you as you talk to your partner.

If you have no experience telling the truth about yourself with friends, don't be in a big hurry to do this assignment. In fact, you might want to wait until we discuss the concept of telling the truth about ourselves to friends on page 65 of *Real Love in Marriage*—on Day Fourteen of this workbook—at which time you may choose to begin to share your assignments with friends.

DAY TWO:

Imitation Love

First Assignment

Share with your partner the Fifth Assignment from Day One. Take your time with this. This is an opportunity for you and your partner to lay down many years—even decades—of blaming and resentment. Talk with each other about how it felt to share these assignments.

Second Assignment

In the meeting, read from the book *Real Love in Marriage*:
Begin   Page 9, Title: What We Use Without Enough Real Love
End   Page 16, Title: What We Do Without Enough Love

(All the following assignments to be done outside the meeting)

Third Assignment

In the following space describe how you have used and traded Imitation Love in your life and in your relationship. Phrase each statement as though you were making it to your partner.

Many people have a difficult time at this point, because being honest about *our own selfish behaviors* is a novel behavior for most of us. Instead, all our lives we've seen the people around us follow the consistent pattern of diligently and energetically describing the flaws of others. For that reason, allow me to provide a few examples of this assignment (many more to be found in the book *Real Love* and in other books of that series):

- I'm always trying to please people, but I'm realizing now that I often do is not for their benefit but for my own. I do it so they'll like me, and it's exhausting and frustrating—for me and for you, because it take a lot of time away from you.

- In most conversations or situations, I insist on being right. I never realized this before, but it gives me a feeling of power, and it is not contributing to the love in our relationship.
- Most of the time—maybe all the time—I care about the pleasure I get from sex, without thinking about whether it's pleasurable for you.
- When things get the least bit tense between us, I just withdraw. I'd rather feel safe than working things out with you and taking the risk of being hurt.
- I buy way more clothes than I need, because I enjoy what people say about me when I look nice. It makes me feel good (praise).
- I criticize you a lot, far more than I need to. I didn't realize until now that it gave me a feeling of control (power).
- Sometimes I give you sex (pleasure) as a way of manipulating you to give me some of the things I want.
- A lot of the time I just watch television because I don't know what to say to you. It's the easiest (safest) thing for me to do.
- For a long time I've been blaming you for no longer being the person I fell in love with, when the truth is, you still have the same qualities you always had. What's happened is that the excitement of those things has just worn off for me. I'm the one who counted on Imitation Love to bring me happiness, but I've blamed the disappointment on you.

You'll be sharing this assignment with your partner tomorrow, on Day Three.

Fourth Assignment

Share your Assignment with a friend, and in the space below describe this experience. For an explanation of sharing with a friend, see the Sixth Assignment of Day One.

DAY THREE:
Getting and Protecting Behaviors

First Assignment

Share with your partner the Third Assignment from Day Two. Don't rush through this. You're creating an opportunity here for your partner to see who you really are, the power of which we'll be explaining further in future pages.

Talk about how it felt to share this assignment with each other.

Second Assignment

In the meeting, read from the book *Real Love in Marriage*:
Begin   Page 16, Title: What We Do Without Enough Love
End   Page 23, Title: The Destructive Effect of Getting and Protecting

(Complete the following assignments outside the meeting.)

Third Assignment

In the following space describe how you have used Getting and Protecting Behaviors in your life and in your relationship. Phrase each statement as though you were making it to your partner. Because this can be a difficult assignment for many people, I will provide a few examples of this assignment (many more to be found in the book *Real Love* and in other books of that series):

- All my life I've agreed with people and told people what they've wanted to hear, so they would like me. I've done that with you too.

- I make excuses all the time for not doing the things you ask me to do. Most of the time I believe my own excuses, but I can see now that I'm just lying to avoid your disapproval.
- I get angry at you more often than I realized before, and certainly much more often than I've ever admitted to you.
- I attack you by making critical comments about the things you do. Way too often.
- Sometimes I complain to my friends and family about the way you treat me. I'm gathering allies to prove I'm right. It's not a loving way for me to behave. I'm acting like a victim, and I'm not proud of it.
- Sometimes instead of simply telling you what I want, I cry or complain to get sympathy from you, so you'll feel like you have to give me what I want. I'm acting like a victim.
- When I get home from work, I often just avoid you. I'm running—and also attacking you in my mind.
- Sometimes I drink more than I should, and it's just to avoid the pain or conflict in my life.
- When I tell you "I love you," I expect you to say "I love you" back. I'm disappointed or annoyed if you don't, so when I say "I love you," I'm really clinging.
- Sometimes you ask me to go out and do stuff with you, and I tell you I'm too busy, or too tired, or too sick, or whatever, but the truth is, I'm just avoiding the conflicts we almost always have. I'm a coward, so I make up excuses.
- I'm always trying to look attractive, so you won't look at other women.

You'll be sharing this assignment with your partner tomorrow, on Day Four.

Fourth Assignment

Share your Third Assignment with a friend, and in the space below describe this experience. For an explanation of sharing with a friend, see the Sixth Assignment of Day One.

DAY FOUR:

The Effects of Getting and Protecting Behaviors

First Assignment

Share with your partner what you wrote for your Third Assignment from Day Three. These can be very tender moments, as the two of you share the flawed behaviors of your lives. As your partner shares his or her Getting and Protecting Behaviors, be careful that you just listen. Do *not* add to his or her observations.

If she describes her lying, for example, you would not want to say, "You sure do lie! Why, just the other day you lied to me . . ." Should you take such an opportunity to "pile on" your observations, you'll bring to an end any honesty and openness your partner might have brought to your interaction. Have faith that your partner is beginning a process of learning that will enrich your relationship.

Talk about how it felt to share this assignment with each other.

Second Assignment

In the meeting, read from the book *Real Love in Marriage*:
Begin   Page 23, Title: The Destructive Effect of Getting and Protecting
End   Page 28, Title: Exercises

(Complete the following assignments outside the meeting.)

Third Assignment

Look again at the list of behaviors you created in the Third Assignment of Day Three. In the following space describe how these behaviors have caused harm to your own happiness, to the happiness of your partner, and to the joy of your relationship. Phrase each statement as though you were making it to your partner. Allow me to provide a few examples of this assignment:

- Whenever I tell you what you want to hear in order to win your approval, the feeling doesn't last long, and I end up feeling frustrated. You probably feel manipulated by me too, so nobody wins.
- I tell you little lies all the time about what I'm doing and where I'm going, and I'm sure you can feel it much of the time. When you do, you must hear me telling you that I don't care about you. When I lie to you, I feel farther apart from you too.
- Every time I get irritated at you, I'm thinking of myself: what you did *to me* or what you should have done *for me*. I'm not thinking about you at all. In fact, I'm sure you hear me shouting at you, "I don't love you," and each time I'm angry, that's true—I'm far too concerned about myself to be caring about you.
- When I criticize so many little things you do, you must feel very unloved by me. I just never realized how much I've undermined you for so very long.
- My negative comments about you to other people have been really unsupportive and unloving. I must have seemed like an enemy to you on many occasions.
- When I whine and complain around you, you must think that I care only about myself and don't think about you at all. I never realized until now that when I whine, I actually feel more isolated and alone myself.
- When I withdraw from you, I feel safer for a while, but I also feel more alone. I'm sure you feel more alone and unloved too, which must be painful.
- When I drink, I dull the pain for a moment, but when I sober up the pain is right there again. And when I drink, you must feel more alone.

You'll be sharing this assignment with your partner tomorrow, on Day Five.

Fourth Assignment

Share your Third Assignment with a friend, and in the space below describe this experience. For an explanation of sharing with a friend, see the Sixth Assignment of Day One.

DAY FIVE:

Eliminating Anger

First Assignment

Share with your partner what you wrote for your Third Assignment from Day Four. I would especially recommend that you share some version of the following: "Every time I'm angry, I'm telling you that I don't love you." When we take responsibility for that truth, it becomes much more difficult to continue in our selfish anger.

Again, these can be very tender moments, because the two of you are finally taking responsibility for the pain you have both experienced and caused for so many years, rather than blaming each other for that pain. After counseling thousands of couples, it has been my experience that people suffer as much from being *blamed* for the pain in each other's lives as they do from the actual pain inflicted by any careless or malicious acts committed by their partners. The force of blaming is horrific. In this assignment you're recognizing the effects of your own Getting and Protecting Behaviors and taking responsibility for them, which removes an enormous burden from your partner's soul.

You might consider repeating this assignment on a regular basis throughout your marriage.

Now talk about how it felt to share this assignment with each other.

Second Assignment

In the meeting, read from the book *Real Love in Marriage*:
Begin   Page 30, Title: The First Steps to Success in Marriage
End   Page 36, to end of last full paragraph, ending with words,
         "... out of the water instead."

(Complete the following assignments outside the meeting.)

Third Assignment

In the space below describe an interaction you have experienced with your partner where he or she behaved in a way that you found annoying or frustrating or difficult to understand, where you thought, Why in the world is he or she acting like this? In light of what you now understand about Real Love and Getting and Protecting Behaviors, describe why your partner was behaving in that way.

Fourth Assignment

On pages 31-36 of *Real Love in Marriage* you learned that people who are behaving badly are simply drowning. People who behave badly are using Getting and Protecting Behaviors, which are only a response to emptiness and fear, conditions that indicate a lack of Real Love—which in turn is as important to all of us emotionally as air is to a drowning man. How does this change the way you *feel* about the event you described in the Third Assignment above?

You'll be sharing your Third and Fourth Assignments with your partner tomorrow, on Day Six.

Fifth Assignment

Share your Third and Fourth Assignments with a friend, and in the space below describe this experience. For an explanation of sharing with a friend, see the Sixth Assignment of Day One.

DAY SIX:
No More Blaming

First Assignment

Share with your partner what you wrote for your Third and Fourth Assignments from Day Five. As with your First Assignment from Day Five, this is another beautiful opportunity for both of you to release—and be released from—the deadly burden of blaming, which destroys so many relationships.

I would especially recommend that sometime during your sharing you say something like the following (in your own words, of course): "I would never be angry at someone for drowning in the water—in an actual lake, for example—and yet during the time we've been together I've been angry at you many times for drowning emotionally. Now I realize how selfish I have been to do that. I probably won't stop that overnight, but I'll certainly be more aware of it."

An intellectual understanding of our partners won't result in an immediate change in our behaviors, but it will help us change the way we feel, and gradually our behavior will change, especially as we continue to be truthful about the times we are angry and selfish.

Now talk about how it felt to share this assignment with each other.

Second Assignment

In the meeting, read from the book *Real Love in Marriage*:
Begin   bottom Page 36, last paragraph, beginning with, "As I
            tell people . . ."
End   Page 40, Title: Overcoming the Frustration . . .

(Complete the following assignments outside the meeting.)

Third Assignment

As we learned from the reading on Day Five, other people never make us angry. Understanding this gives us enormous freedom. Now we have a choice. We could spend our entire lives trying to keep people from taking two emotional dollars from us—from doing all the little things in our lives that potentially could be annoying—but down that road lies nothing but misery. It's just not possible to stop everyone from doing all the little annoying things they'll do, and even if we could, we'd be utterly exhausted from the never ending effort. How much wiser we would be to simply build up a store of twenty million dollars—which is how we feel when we have enough Real Love—at which point it simply would not matter when people made their little mistakes around us.

Remember how you felt during the meditation on pages 6-7 of *Real Love in Marriage*? When we feel that loved, the little mistakes our spouses make really don't annoy us, which proves that our spouses are not the cause of our irritation.

Make a written commitment below that you will not blame your partner for your anger but instead will take complete responsibility for it yourself. Now make a silent commitment to share that with him or her at your next meeting, on Day Seven.

You'll be sharing this assignment with your partner tomorrow, on Day Seven.

Fourth Assignment

Just as *other people* behave badly because *they* are drowning, so also do *you* behave badly because *you* are drowning. Are you willing to allow yourself some tolerance for your own mistakes? This is not to make *excuses* for your behavior but simply to *understand* yourself better, so you don't wallow in unnecessary guilt, which detracts from your ability to be loving, the quality you wish to bring into your relationships.

In the space below describe a situation where you behaved badly toward your partner. Now try to recall whether you felt unconditionally loved on that occasion. Were you drowning? Were you down to your last two dollars? Now is it more understandable to you why you behaved in the way you did? Now can you be more accepting of yourself? Without making excuses for your behavior, can you lighten up on the guilt and move on with the healthy process of simply learning to change your behavior and become a more loving partner?

Fifth Assignment

Share your Third and Fourth Assignments with a friend, and in the space below describe this experience. For an explanation of sharing with a friend, see the Sixth Assignment of Day One.

DAY SEVEN:
The Law of Choice

First Assignment

Share with your partner what you wrote for your Third Assignment from Day Six. It is fully expected that you will both fail to keep the commitment in this assignment on many occasions. That's all right. We learn and grow as we make commitments, make mistakes, and get up off the ground to try all the harder to keep those commitments again. Failing doesn't make us bad. It makes us human.

Now talk about how it felt to share this assignment with each other.

Second Assignment

In the meeting, read from the book *Real Love in Marriage*:
Begin   Page 40, Title: Overcoming the Frustration . . .
End   Page 41, Title: Honoring The Law of Choice . . .

(Complete the following assignments outside the meeting.)

Third Assignment

When we get deep into the confusion of Getting and Protecting Behaviors, sometimes it can seem that there is no way out of the darkness and the pain. And when we're first learning the principles of Real Love—when we first pick up the 337-page *Real Love in Marriage* book, for example—the process of change can seem a bit overwhelming.

But the principles of Real Love are actually quite simple. The application of them may not be *easy*, because we're working against the habits of a lifetime, but the principles themselves are few and simple. Consider the meat of what we've learned thus far:

- Real Love is unconditional, without disappointment or anger.
- Nearly all of us—roughly 98% of us, without exaggeration—were raised without sufficient Real Love in our lives, which has left us feeling empty and afraid much of the time.
- We react to our emptiness and fear with Getting and Protecting Behaviors, which temporarily make us feel better—by way of Imitation Love—but always end up hurting us and the people around us.
- Other people are never responsible for our anger, nor for any of our other negative feelings.
- Every time we're angry—or when we use any of our other Getting and Protecting Behavior—we're saying to the people around us, "I don't love you.'

These are not complicated principles, and when we remember them we loose the chains that tie us to the anger, victimhood, and other feelings and behaviors that destroy our happiness and relationships. There are only a few other founding principles that are key to our happiness and our relationships, and one of them is found in the pages above: The Law of Choice. Without preservation of the Law of Choice *no one* could be happy. Ever. If you doubt that, reread pages 40-41. We never have the right to control the choices of our partners (with the rare exceptions of cases like our partners being in a coma, for those of you who are lawyers). The instant I control you, we don't have a relationship anymore, and is that what I really want?

In the following space describe a situation where you were angry at your partner. Then describe how your anger was really a reaction to your inability to control your partner. Next describe what you realize about the selfishness and the destructive consequences of your efforts to control your partner's right to make his or her own choices.

You'll be sharing this assignment with your partner tomorrow, on Day Eight.

Fourth Assignment

Share your Third Assignment with a friend, and in the space below describe this experience. For an explanation of sharing with a friend, see the Sixth Assignment of Day One.

DAY EIGHT:
The Three Choices

First Assignment

Share with your partner what you wrote for your Third Assignment from Day Seven. Obviously, what you share is your business, but you'll tend to find it effective—for you and for your partner—if at some point you can say something like the following (in your own words, of course):

"Every time I get angry at you—or lie to you, or act like a victim, or use any Getting and Protecting Behavior with you—I'm trying to control your choices. I'm trying to control *who you are*, which is pretty unloving. I must say I hadn't realized that until studying these principles, but it's still true. I also can't say I'll immediately stop it, but I'll certainly be more aware of it."

Talk about how it felt to share this assignment with each other.

Second Assignment

In the meeting, read from the book *Real Love in Marriage*:
Begin   Page 41, Title: Honoring The Law of Choice . . .
End   Page 45, Title: Identifying What We Need to Change

(Complete the following assignments outside the meeting.)

Third Assignment

The three choices are useful in every situation, and since "living with it and hating it" is obviously unproductive—stupid, really, since it always leads to unhappiness—we can eliminate that immediately, and we are left with just two choices:

- Live with it and like it
- Leave it

With these two choices and the basics of Real Love, many previously knotty problems resolve nicely. Let's look at a longstanding argument that occurred between Fred and Susie, for example. Susie had complained for years that Fred hated to visit her family and never went with her to family gatherings. Fred argued that Susie's family was boring, judgmental, stupid, and so on. These arguments go on and on.

"As it is now," I suggested, "you're both choosing to live with it and hate it, right?"

They both agreed.

"Would you like to change what you have now and be happy instead?" I asked.

Again, they agreed, and I suggested that we could look at the two choices.

"Fred," I said, "this has nothing to do with Susie's family. It has everything to do with Real Love. Are you willing to do something here to demonstrate that you care about her happiness?"

"But I *hate* being around those people," he said.

"I completely understand that," I said. "I'm not asking you to like them. I'm asking you to look at this in a completely different way, from a completely different perspective. Are you willing to look at a visit to her family's house as an opportunity to support and love *Susie*? It would be a loving *gift* to her. Now, before you answer that, when she goes over there, how long does she stay?"

Fred rolled his eyes and sighed before he spoke. "Like forever. All day. Hours and hours. It never ends."

"Okay, so that's part of the problem. You can't stand being there all day. You might consider combining the two choices we've discussed: living with it and liking it *and* leaving it. The two of you, for example, might travel separately to the family event in two cars. That's one option. *Or* you both might go over there in one car, then you—Fred—could return home in your car and have one of her family members bring her back home later in the day or evening. With either of those options, the moment you felt overwhelmed, you could come back home. You'd never feel trapped, as you do now."

"But she'd get mad if I left early," Fred said.

"That's *her* choice," I said. "Whatever time you spend there with her is *your* unconditionally loving gift to her, and then she gets to make one of the three choices in response. I would hope she would receive the gift and feel loved by it. Susie, would you rather that Fred went and spent *some time* with you and your family or *no time*?"

"I never thought about it as a gift like that," she said. "I guess I *would* rather he came for any time at all."

They both smiled. With Real Love and an understanding of choices, their problem was solved.

In the following space describe a problem you've been having in your relationship and outline how you could improve it using the three choices we've discussed. This can be a difficult assignment, so allow me to provide a few more examples:

- When I come in the living room and you're watching television, I get irritated. I want you to stop watching and talk to me. That choice (live with it and hate it) is stupid. On those occasions I either need to sit next to you and enjoy your company (live with it and like it) or leave the room (leave it).

- Sometimes when I'm in a store with you, you end up shopping far longer than you said you would, and I get very impatient. Living with it and hating it only ruins my day and affects our relationship badly. I need to either make a decision to enjoy our time together—which I usually can't do—or prepare ahead of time to enjoy myself. For example, I could bring a book with me in the car, and when I get tired of shopping, I could excuse myself to go to the car, where I could read the book. I'd be a lot happier.

- Sometimes you make the most obnoxious noises—when you eat or just sitting around. Being irritated by them and nagging you about them has only made me unhappy. Only two choices make any sense. I could accept those noises as part of the overall package of who you are and love the whole package. Or, on the occasions when the noises are distracting, I could simply leave the room and not be irritated by you personally.

- In the past I have often felt pressured by you to have sex, and on many occasions I have given in and had sex with you reluctantly, which is ridiculous, because then I'm sure it has not been nearly as fun for you. Instead I just need to make a decision to have sex freely and gladly (live with it and like it) or just say *no* (leave it) and tell you that I'd rather not on that particular occasion.

You'll be sharing this assignment with your partner tomorrow, on Day Nine.

Fourth Assignment

Share your Third Assignment with a friend, and in the space below describe this experience. For an explanation of sharing with a friend, see the Sixth Assignment of Day One.

DAY NINE:
Taking Responsibility for Ourselves

First Assignment

Share with your partner what you wrote for your Third Assignment from Day Eight. You'll discover that making rational, sensible choices with and about your partner is so much more loving and enjoyable than arguing with and struggling against him or her.

Talk about how it felt to share this assignment with each other.

Second Assignment

In the meeting, read from the book *Real Love in Marriage*:
Begin   Page 45, Title: Identifying What We Need to Change
End   Page 46, Title: The Law of Expectations

Third Assignment (to be completed in this day's meeting)

You've had enough experience with the principles of Real Love to this point that you can probably do this assignment spontaneously—on the spot, as it were—with your partner. If you're doing the 40 days alone, you can do this assignment as a one-man play, pretending that your partner is present in the room with you.

When we believe that other people cause our feelings and behavior, we become enslaved by those people, and we must free ourselves from this lie if we wish to live happily. We have already discussed the principles that will give us this freedom, and it can be very helpful for us to speak the words of these truths to our partners. There is an empowerment that comes with speaking aloud what we know to be true, especially to those we interact with regularly. This act somehow commits us to live according to the knowledge we possess.

Toward that end, read to your partner the following bulleted items. Allow a pause between each one, long enough for it to sink in for your partner. If there is any particular item that you just can't say—you don't quite believe it yet, or it's just too painful—skip it. You may be able to say it at a later time.

- When I get angry at you, that is never your fault. Instead it's a sign that I'm feeling empty or afraid, or both.
- When I lie to you or make excuses, I'm protecting myself or trying to get something for myself. It's all about me, not you.
- When I avoid you or withdraw from you, that is not your fault. I'm feeling empty and afraid as a result of a lifetime of not feeling loved—although in the moment I may believe I'm reacting to you.
- When I act hurt by you, I'm reacting to the pain of a lifetime of not feeling loved—including long before I met you—not just to what you did in any given moment. And my feeling hurt is always a choice.

Take your time with this. If you can say these words with sincerity, you may begin or accelerate profound healing in your relationship. Love simply cannot bloom in soil that is seeded with the insidious poison of blame. As you take responsibility for your own feelings and behavior—and in the process tell your partner that he or she is not to blame for your pain, your anger, and your other negative feelings and behaviors—you cleanse the soil of your relationship from this poison. Instead you sow the seeds of truth, responsibility, and trust, and the harvest you will reap will be rich indeed.

DAY TEN:

The Law of Expectations

First Assignment

In the meeting, read from the book *Real Love in Marriage*:
Begin   Page 46, Title: The Law of Expectations
End   Page 49, end of page

(Complete the following assignments outside the meeting.)

Second Assignment

In the following space:

A. Describe a situation where you felt angry at your partner—or hurt by or frustrated at him or her.
B. Now that you understand expectations, describe how *you* first had an expectation—or expectations—of some kind *before* you felt hurt, frustrated, or angry.
C. In light of your new understanding of the Law of Expectations, discuss how you now see your pain, frustration, or anger.

Your description will likely be longer, but allow me to provide a couple of brief examples of this assignment:

Example 1:

A. I've been so angry—on many occasions—that my wife has been late to everything and has made me wait.
B. Even though she's always been more of a creative, disorganized, right-brained person her whole life, when *I'm* involved—center of the universe that I am—I expect her to suddenly become exact, meticulous, and punctual.
C. It's not my wife that's the problem here. It's my expectations that are selfish and crazy.

Example 2:

A. I've been frustrated and hurt that my husband never spends time
    with me. I nagged him about it two days ago.
B. I don't think about *why* he doesn't spend time with me. I don't
    care about *his* emptiness or fears. Instead I just have *expectations*
    about what he will do for *me*.
C. If I were to see his needs, my expectations would disappear.

You'll be sharing this assignment with your partner tomorrow, on
Day Eleven.

Third Assignment

Share your Second with a friend, and in the space below describe this experience. For an explanation of sharing with a friend, see the Sixth Assignment of Day One.

DAY ELEVEN:
Telling the Truth

First Assignment

Share with your partner what you wrote for your Second Assignment from Day Ten. This will be most effective if you don't make excuses for your expectations, which are selfish and violate the Law of Choice. Follow the general pattern of the examples provided above, and you'll tend to do well.

Talk about how it felt to share this assignment with each other.

Second Assignment

In the meeting, read from the book *Real Love in Marriage*:
Begin   Page 52, Title: Taking Action
End   Page 56, Title: Telling the Truth About Yourself to Your
            Spouse

(Complete the following assignments outside the meeting.)

Third Assignment

A. In the following space list some of the feelings you experience and the behaviors you demonstrate that interfere with your happiness and with the joy of your relationship. You know what they are. These harmful behaviors are all variations on the Getting and Protecting Behaviors we've already discussed.

B. Now list some of the feelings your partner experiences and the behaviors he or she demonstrates that interfere with his or her happiness and with the joy of your relationship.

C. Are you content to continue with your present course of choices, the ones that are producing the above feelings and behaviors? Yes or no?

Would you like to eliminate the feelings and behaviors that are interfering with the happiness of you and your partner? Real Love has the power to eliminate all these feelings and behaviors, so you can then fill your life and relationship with joy. Delightfully, finding this love and joy is not complicated. It's not a convoluted process of six or eight intellectual steps. It's just a single step: telling the truth about yourself. Initially that step can be frightening, to be sure, but once taken, the results can be rather immediate and dramatic, as they were for the Wart King.

D. Are you willing to make the commitment to take that initial step
of being truthful about yourself with your partner, so you can
make possible the process

Truth → Seen → Accepted → Loved

that is described in *Real Love in Marriage*? If so, indicate your
commitment in writing below.

You'll be sharing Parts, A, C, and D of this assignment with your
partner tomorrow, on Day Twelve.

Fourth Assignment

Share your Third Assignment with a friend, and in the space below
describe this experience. For an explanation of sharing with a friend,
see the Sixth Assignment of Day One.

DAY TWELVE:
Telling the Truth to Our Partners

First Assignment

Share with your partner what you wrote for your Third Assignment—Parts A, C, and D only—from Day Eleven. Do *not* share Part B, because our relationships are generally not enriched as we share with our partners *their* negative feelings and behaviors—with some exceptions, which we will discuss beginning on Day Thirty-Seven. Most important is your commitment to begin the process of being increasingly truthful about *yourself* with your partner (Part D). Don't be overly anxious about this. You've already begun the process of truth telling, as you completed the assignments of Days 1, 2, 3, 4, 5, 7, 9, and 10.

Talk about how it felt to share this assignment with each other.

Second Assignment

In the meeting, read from the book *Real Love in Marriage*:
Begin   Page 56, Title: Telling the Truth About Yourself to Your Spouse
End   Page 62, end of first paragraph, " . . . see, accept, and love you."

(Complete the following assignments outside the meeting.)

Third Assignment

Real Love is THE element that will make the biggest difference in our relationships. It eliminates conflict, heals wounds, and introduces a level of joy and excitement that most of us have never imagined. Anything we can do to introduce that quality into our relationships is worth whatever effort we make. Fortunately, we only have to begin with telling the truth about ourselves.

In Day Eleven you made the commitment to begin this process, and in previous Days you actually practiced telling the truth. In the following space discuss a situation or two where you may have been less than entirely honest with your partner. Then describe what it would look like for you to be completely honest about that situation. Make these statements as though you were speaking to your partner.

You can find four examples of how to complete this assignment on page 61 of *Real Love in Marriage*. In each of these examples in the book, however, the untruthful behavior is hypothetical, referring to what *might* happen. You'll be describing an actual situation. Allow me to offer a couple of examples of completing this assignment:

- When I got home late from work, you asked me why I was late, and I just mumbled something. You persisted, so I got irritated. I said, "Do I have to explain myself every time I walk in the door?" The truth is, I didn't want to have to tell you what really happened. I made some mistakes at work and got behind. Then I had to stay late, but if I had been thinking about you, I could easily have called you and told you that I would be late. But I was selfish and didn't think about you at all. I was only thinking about myself, and I'm sorry. Next time I'll try to be more thoughtful.

- The other day when you opened the fridge, you asked me where the hot dogs were, and I said I didn't know. I lied. I had made some for the kids the day before, and I knew when I did it that you hated it when we ran out of hot dogs, but I used them all up anyway. I could have gotten some at the store almost immediately to replace them—I drove right by there—but I just didn't do it. Then when you asked about it, I was too embarrassed to tell you the truth. The truth is, I didn't think about what you wanted, and then I lied to cover up my mistake.

You'll be sharing this assignment with your partner tomorrow, on Day Thirteen.

Fourth Assignment

Share your Third Assignment with a friend, and in the space below describe this experience. For an explanation of sharing with a friend, see the Sixth Assignment of Day One.

DAY THIRTEEN:

Telling the Truth to Our Partners— Again

First Assignment

Share with your partner what you wrote for your Third Assignment from Day Twelve. It can be such fun to finally tell the truth about ourselves to our partners—and to hear our partners tell the truth about themselves—can it not? Most of us have been living in the twilight and darkness of lies for so long that the truth is a refreshing peek into the light.

Talk about how it felt to share this assignment with each other.

Second Assignment

In the meeting, read from the book *Real Love in Marriage*:

Begin   Page 62, second paragraph, "Every time we talk to our spouses . . ."

End   Page 65, Title: Telling the Truth About Yourself to People . . .

(Complete the following assignments outside the meeting.)

Third Assignment

In the following space describe a recent situation where you were irritated toward your partner, or where you were blaming him or her for something that happened. Then describe how it might look for you to be truthful about that situation, taking complete responsibility for your own feelings—recognizing that other people never cause how we feel or behave and that we can always choose to be honest and loving. You'll find several examples of this assignment on pages 64-5.

You'll be sharing this assignment with your partner tomorrow, on Day Fourteen.

Fourth Assignment

Share your Third Assignment with a friend, and in the space below describe this experience. For an explanation of sharing with a friend, see the Sixth Assignment of Day One.

DAY FOURTEEN:
Telling the Truth to Other People

First Assignment

Share with your partner what you wrote for your Third Assignment from Day Thirteen.

Talk about how it felt to share this assignment with each other.

Second Assignment

In the meeting, read from the book *Real Love in Marriage*:

Begin	Page 65, Title: Telling the Truth About Yourself to People
End	Page 69, Title: Finding a Wise Man
Begin	Page 77, Title: The Effect on Your Marriage of the Real Love . . .
End	Page 80, Title: Group Meetings

Third Assignment (still in the meeting)

I have now had the opportunity of observing many hundreds of couples learning to introduce Real Love into their relationships. As you practice telling the truth about yourself with your partner, I can tell you that it is very likely that you will experience with your partner some variation on the following three scenarios:

A. He or she will steadily respond with increasing measures of Real Love. The two of you will become such an abundant source of unconditional love for each other that you will literally revolutionize each other's lives and will not often need another source of Real Love outside your marriage. This is most uncommon.

B. He or she will be unconditionally accepting on some occasions but be quite incapable of offering Real Love on other occasions. These latter moments will sometimes prove to be quite frustrating to you, since you will have developed a taste for Real Love.

C. He or she will be virtually incapable of unconditionally loving you and uninterested in the process.

It is also not uncommon for relationships to move back and forth between these three conditions over periods of months, weeks, and even days. Whatever the ability of your partner to be loving, it is never wise to rely on him or her for your entire supply of Real Love, just as it is unwise for any of us to rely on a single source of financial income or for a manufacturer to rely on a single supplier for his sole source of a critical raw material. If you rely on your partner for all your Real Love, for example, and he or she has a bad day for whatever reason, you'll feel entirely cut off from your vital supply of unconditional love. That will not be a good day for you.

We all need as many sources of Real Love as possible, and that is why we need to explore loving relationships with people other than our partners. This is not a form of disloyalty to your partner but actually a rich resource that will bless your relationship, as illustrated on pages 66-8 by Marilyn and Angela. It's important to understand that telling the truth about yourself to another person should never affect your loyalty—sexual or otherwise—to your partner, a subject that is covered in more detail on pages 74-6 of *Real Love in Marriage*.

Discuss with your partner the following:

1. Are you willing to tell the truth about yourself to other people and find other sources of Real Love to bring back to your relationship?

2. You need to understand that as your partner tells the truth about himself or herself, on occasion it will be necessary for him or her to make references to *your* behavior, just to provide *context* for talking about his or her Getting and Protecting Behaviors—as you saw in the case of Marilyn. This is unavoidable. Remembering the Law of Choice, express to your partner your support of him or her as he or she embarks

on the adventure of telling the truth about himself or herself to other people. Your partner will be doing this in the hope of bringing more Real Love back to your relationship, which will directly benefit you. We'll talk more about how to find these wise men and women on Day Fifteen.

DAY FIFTEEN:

Finding and Talking to Wise Men and Women

First Assignment

In the meeting, read from the book *Real Love in Marriage*:
Begin   Page 69, Title: Finding a Wise Man
End   Page 80, Title: The Power of Real Love

(Complete the following assignments outside the meeting.)

Second Assignment

From Day Two I have been giving you a repeated assignment, which reads as follows:

> Share your assignment with a friend, and in the following space describe this experience. For an explanation of sharing with a friend, see the Sixth Assignment of Day One.

Then in the Sixth Assignment of Day One I explained that if you had no experience with telling the truth about yourself with friends, I would explain this concept later in the workbook. I began that explanation with the reading on Day Fourteen, and it continues with the reading above, in pages 69-80.

On Day Eleven we talked about the importance of truth telling in the following process

Truth → Seen → Accepted → Loved

as you create opportunities for both of you to feel accepted and loved by *each other*. It is equally important that you create opportunities for *other people*—for friends, family members, and others—to accept and love you, so you can bring this love back to your relationship.

Where can we find these wise men and women who will love us unconditionally? We find them everywhere we tell the truth, but the above pages will be quite helpful in answering this question, as will the resources on pages 325-7 of *Real Love in Marriage*. The website at www.RealLove.com is also being constantly updated to provide even more resources for people to find wise men and women.

In the space below list some people who you imagine might be capable of accepting you as you tell the truth about yourself. By "accepting you," I mean listening without being judgmental or without joining you in acting like a victim.

Third Assignment

Using the examples of truth telling you have read thus far in the book for inspiration—and also examples in other Real Love books or on the RealLove.com website, if you have read or viewed those—use the following space to tell the truth about some instances when you have used Getting and Protecting Behaviors with your partner. This is similar to the Third Assignment of Day Three, except that now you have considerably more understanding, and you will be describing more specific scenarios in greater detail, rather than generalizing.

Because this can be difficult for many people, allow me to provide a few examples:

- Yesterday my wife was watching television, and when I came into the room, she asked me if there was anything I wanted to watch. What I wanted to do was go for a walk with her, but I didn't have the courage to interrupt her television watching to ask for what I wanted. I'm afraid of potential confrontations and rejections, so I lied and said *no*, and then I withdrew into the next room.

- Two days ago my husband asked me if I'd picked something up from the store that he'd asked me to get, and I told him that I'd been extra busy all day and hadn't had a chance to do it yet. But the truth is, I just forgot. I lied to him.

- This morning my wife ate some leftovers from the fridge that I had planned on eating myself, and I got irritated at her about it. I was mad for hours, blaming her for my anger, when the truth is that I was just being selfish, demanding something for myself that she had every right to. I was also expecting her to read my mind about it. I do that a lot.

- I realized that today I walked around for much of the day angry at my husband because he had done this thing or that thing *to me*, when I could have made the choice to see him as drowning. I could have made the choice to love him and been much happier. But I didn't.

- Yesterday I said several things to my wife about her driving, when all I had to do was shut my mouth, and we could have had a perfectly pleasant drive together. I ruined the whole thing with my mouth, but I blamed her for the argument we had. It was my fault.

- Yesterday I talked to my mother on the phone about how my husband doesn't do enough for me or spend enough time with me. I realized that I have been poisoning my mother against my husband for years, and in the process I make myself feel like a victim all the time too. I'm sure my husband picks up on my attitude too, and then he wants to be around me even less. Nobody wins.

- Today when I got home from work, I noticed that my wife was in a bad mood, so I just went into the next room and read a magazine. I stayed away from her. Now I realize that if she was in a bad mood, what she needed was some loving attention from me, but I was too selfish to give it to her.

You'll be sharing this assignment with your partner tomorrow, on Day Sixteen.

Fourth Assignment

The purpose of the Third Assignment was to give you some practice with telling the truth about yourself in an environment where you would feel the least fear—by yourself. Call or sit down with one of those friends you listed in your Second Assignment and actually share one or two of the truths you listed in the Third Assignment. You don't need to make this a formal affair, where you say, "I've come to tell you the truth about myself." Truth telling can be quite casual, done in the context of talking about the events of the day.

Think about it. When we're with our friends, we talk about the little things we do all the time. We talk about how we feel, too, including our negative feelings, but as you fulfill this assignment, instead of blaming your partner for how you feel, you're going to take responsibility for it. Let me use the last example from the Third Assignment above and demonstrate how easily you can work truth telling into a conversation.

You and your friend Bob talk about work and football for a while, and then you say, "How are things with Joyce (your friend's wife)?"

"Oh, all right, I guess," he says. "Same old stuff. Nothin' different. How's Kristin (your wife)?"

"Not bad. The older I get, the more I'm learning about being a better husband. It's taken me long enough. A few days ago when I got home from work, I noticed that she was in a bad mood, so I just went into the next room and read a magazine. I stayed away from her. That's what I usually do. It's easier. But I'm beginning to realize that if she is in a bad mood, there's a message there. What she needs is some positive attention from me, and I've always been too selfish to give it to her. I decided to pay attention to what she needs, so yesterday when she was in a bad mood, I hugged her and asked her about her day instead of being selfish and disappearing into the next room. Wow, what a difference it made. It's like she became a different person."

What if your friend Bob looks at you like you've gone utterly insane? What if he can't think of a single thing to say after you've completely ruined the conversation for him? You haven't lost anything. You've just learned that Bob isn't interested in hearing the truth about you, so you can return to talking about football, and Bob will be grateful.

But what if Bob says, "Hey, that's amazing honesty. Nobody takes responsibility for their selfishness like that. Where'd you learn to do that? Joyce would love it if I did that."

At this point you have learned two remarkable things:

1. Your friend has accepted you *while* you were telling him that you were selfish toward your wife. That is a moment of unconditional acceptance—a moment of Real Love—and you created the opportunity for that moment simply by telling the truth.
2. You have received virtually an invitation to make another attempt at telling the truth with this friend.

This is not a one-time assignment, but one that continues for a lifetime. You'll be finding wise men and women to share yourself with all your life, and you'll find them in a wide variety of places, some of which were mentioned in the Second Assignment above.

Fifth Assignment

It should be noted that another source of Real Love in the lives of many people is Divine, whether people refer to that source as God or a Greater Power or by another name. As they meditate or pray—and especially as they tell the truth about themselves during their meditation or prayer—they create the opportunity to feel connected to that Divine source of love, and for some people that can become the greatest source of all.

Because of the potential importance of this Divine Source of love, consider which of the following choices you would like to make, if any:

- I would like to meditate and/or pray individually on a regular basis and keep the results of these experiences to myself.
- I would like to meditate and/or pray individually on a regular basis and share the results of these experiences with my partner.
- I would like to meditate and/or pray individually on a regular basis and share the results of these experiences with my partner. Moreover, I would like to meditate and/or pray jointly with my partner.

- I don't want anything to do with meditation and/or prayer.
- I have a different plan regarding meditation and/or prayer, which I will detail in the space below.

You'll be sharing this assignment with your partner tomorrow, on Day Sixteen.

DAY SIXTEEN:
Feeling the Power of Real Love— Gratitude

First Assignment

Share with your partner what you wrote for your Third Assignment from Day Fifteen. Treasure each of these truth telling experiences with your partner. They all spin living threads that can be used to create a most beautiful tapestry.

Talk about how it felt to share this assignment with each other.

Second Assignment

Share with your partner what you wrote for your Fifth Assignment from Day Fifteen. You may notice that your partner may express a desire for less involvement in meditation and/or prayer than you might wish. We'll talk more about conflict resolution on another Day, but for now accept this suggestion that as a loving partner, you would never require your partner to do more for you than he or she freely chooses.

For the purpose of illustration, let's imagine that you choose the most involved option from the Fifth Assignment:

I would like to meditate and/or pray individually on a regular basis and share the results of these experiences with my partner. Moreover, I would like to meditate and/or pray jointly with my partner.

Your partner, on the other hand, chooses the least involved option: "I don't want anything to do with meditation and/or prayer." If you wish to be loving, you couldn't possibly push your partner to do some form of meditation and/or prayer with you. You'd have to do that on your own.

Third Assignment

In the meeting, read from the book *Real Love in Marriage*:
Begin   Page 80, Title: The Power of Real Love
End   Page 83, Title: Sharing Real Love

(Complete the following assignments outside the meeting.)

Fourth Assignment

While it's true that we become happier as we acquire more Real Love in our lives, often we don't need to go out and actually get more love to greatly magnify the joy we're experiencing. Instead on many occasions we can increase our happiness significantly simply by *appreciating* the love we already have.

In the following space describe the evidences of love that you recognize and are grateful for.

Allow me to provide a few examples. Notice that these are more thoughtful than, say, "I'm grateful that you gave me an ice cream cone," because such an act could have been performed for other than genuinely loving reasons. Someone may have given you an ice cream cone just to shut you up, for example, because you were whining incessantly.

- Despite the fact that I've been lying to my wife, angry at her, acting like a victim with her, and withdrawing from her for most of the years we've been married, somehow she keeps recovering and indicating that she's willing to forgive me. I don't know how she does it, but I'm sure thankful for it.
- I'm grateful that my husband has been willing to read the *Real Love in Marriage* book with me.
- I'm grateful that as we have done these exercises in the 40 days, my husband has been willing to tell the truth about himself so many times. That has taken real courage on his part.
- As I have told the truth about myself during these 40 days, my wife has been remarkably accepting of my flaws and selfishness on many occasions. I'm thankful for that
- I have not been easy to live with for many years: selfish, resistant, angry, demanding. And despite a lot of reasons to

leave, my wife has demonstrated a remarkable commitment to stay with me. I'm deeply grateful for that.

- I'm thankful for God's love, which has been there no matter what I've done.
- I appreciate my brother, who has always listened to me, given me good counsel, and not let me act like a victim.
- My mother has always supported me, even when I was rebellious and ungrateful, and I'm grateful to her for that.

You'll be sharing this assignment with your partner tomorrow, on Day Seventeen.

Fifth Assignment

Read your Fourth Assignment at least a couple of times. In the space below answer the following questions:

- How does it feel to emphasize what you're grateful for?
- Can you feel an increased connection to those for whom you feel gratitude, including your partner?
- Can you feel an increase in love from those people?
- Do you feel happier as a result?

You'll be sharing this assignment with your partner tomorrow, on Day Seventeen.

Sixth Assignment

Share your Fourth and Fifth Assignments with a friend, and in the space below describe this experience.

DAY SEVENTEEN:
Learning to Love Our Partners

First Assignment

Share with your partner what you wrote for your Fourth Assignment from Day Sixteen. It would probably be wise to do this only if some of the items listed in your assignment involve gratitude toward your partner.

Discuss the following:

- As you discuss with your partner his or her qualities or behaviors for which you are grateful, how do you feel?
  - Do you feel an increased sense of connection toward your partner?
  - Do you feel more loved by your partner?
  - Do you feel more loving *toward* your partner?
- As your partner discusses *your* qualities and behaviors for which he or she is grateful, how do you feel?
  - Do you feel an increased sense of connection toward your partner?
  - Do you feel more loved by your partner?
  - Do you feel more loving *toward* your partner?
- Do both of you get a sense of how being grateful is so much more rewarding to your relationship than criticism ever could be?

Second Assignment

In the meeting, read from the book *Real Love in Marriage*:
Begin   Page 83, Title: Sharing Real Love
End   Page 87, Title: Loving Acts

(Complete the following assignments outside the meeting.)

Third Assignment

As described in the above pages, we can acquire the ability to love our partners in a variety of ways. We can

- learn to tell the truth about ourselves and find more Real Love for ourselves. In the process, we gradually lose the need to use Getting and Protecting Behaviors, and instead we can see, accept, and love our partners. This process is described in the linear diagram Loved → Seeing → Accepting → Loving or in the circular version of the same diagram, as found on page 85 of *Real Love in Marriage*.
- intellectually learn to see our partners clearly—as empty and afraid, for example—and make the choice to reach out to love and help them instead of reacting to them selfishly. You learned to do this when you learned the metaphor of the drowning man on pages 31-33 of *Real Love in Marriage*.
- simply learn that our Getting and Protecting Behaviors are destructive to ourselves and others, and that loving is always a conscious, infinitely more productive choice that we can make in any given circumstance.

In the following space describe some occasions when you have been influenced by any or all of the learning processes above, as well as how your relationship has been rewarded by these influences. Allow me to provide a few examples of this assignment:

- Two days ago my husband was raising his voice at me, and in the past I would have blown up right back at him. But I remembered that if he's angry, he's just drowning—he's just empty and afraid—so instead I touched him on the arm gently and said a couple of kind words. His anger dissolved like sugar in the rain. No kidding, it was kind of amazing.
- In the first sixteen days that we've been studying this workbook, I've been telling the truth about myself to my wife, and she's expressed more unconditional acceptance of who I really am than I've ever heard. It's been wonderful. I've actually felt loved, and as a result I've been able to be more loving toward *her*.

- Several times in the past couple of days I've felt this urge to get angry, or to act like a victim, but on each of those occasions I've thought about how those behaviors have never worked in the past. They've always made me unhappy and caused terrible feelings between myself and my husband. So I simply made a choice: I chose to shut up and say something loving to him instead. It worked.

You'll be sharing the above assignment with your partner tomorrow, on Day Eighteen.

Fourth Assignment

Share your Third Assignment with a friend, and in the following space describe this experience.

DAY EIGHTEEN:
Loving Acts—Listening

First Assignment

Share with your partner what you wrote for your Third Assignment from Day Seventeen. Discuss how you both feel as you fulfill this assignment and listen with an open heart as your partner talks about the effects that Real Love has been having on him or her and on your relationship.

Second Assignment

In the meeting, read from the book *Real Love in Marriage*:
Begin   Page 87, Title: Loving Acts
End   Page 95, Title: Look

(Complete the following assignments outside the meeting.)

Third Assignment

In the following space describe two issues or situations where your partner has indicated that you have not listened to him or her, where your conversations have often led to conflict between you. Allow me to provide a couple of examples:

1. She's always telling me that we never do anything together, but then I tell her that that's not true. Just two weeks ago I took her to the tractor pull. And yesterday I invited her to sit and watch World Wresting on television with me. So I guess I don't know what she's fussing about.

2. He tells me we never have sex, but what an exaggeration. Just two weeks ago we had sex, and I didn't complain a bit, so how can he say we *never* have sex.

You'll be sharing this assignment with your partner tomorrow, on Day Nineteen.

Fourth Assignment

On a 3 x 5 card write the following

- Be quiet
- Express your acceptance nonverbally
- Avoid verbal criticism
- Restate what you hear—Eight
- Ask questions
- Agree where possible

Using the principles listed on this card—and as described on pages 88-95 of *Real Love in Marriage*—use the following space to describe how you would listen more effectively to the issues or situations described in the Third Assignment.

Allow me to provide a couple of examples, continuing from those I used in the Third Assignment:

1. When she tells me we never do anything together,
   - I don't really *listen*. I *defend* myself, and she can see it in every fiber of my being. I get animated. My voice rises. My posture is defensive. I start talking instead of listening. So, for one thing, I need to just shut up and listen.
   - I need to just tell her that I agree with her. After all, it's mostly true, and I'm just quibbling over the details. She'd fall over backward.
   - I should *ask* her what *she'd like* to do instead of telling her what I've already done with her or what I want to do.
   - I'm missing the real point she's trying to make. She's not really talking about *doing something* together. She could "do something" with her sister. What she's really saying is that she doesn't feel like I care about her. I hardly ever take her anywhere, I don't look her in the eye when I talk to her, I don't sit down and have meaningful conversations with her. In a hundred ways I show her that I don't really care about her. That's the *eight* that she's trying to communicate to me.

2. When he tells me that we never have sex,
   - I get very defensive and argue with him. I'm much more interested in being *right* than I am in actually listening to what he's saying.

- I don't think about how *he* feels. From his perspective, it probably *does* feel like we never have sex. He'd like to have sex three times a day, so having sex every couple of weeks—or less, come to think of it, if I really told the truth—probably does feels like never.
- I need to just say, "You're right, we don't have sex very often. And when we do, it's like I make you *beg* for it. When was the last time I *initiated* sex? Before the Civil War? So at the very least it must seem like I never *want* sex, which couldn't be fun for you."
- I need to ask him how often he'd like sex. More than that, I need to tell him that I'm going to make a point of *initiating* sex more often and asking him more often *what kind* of sex he'd like to have. That would have to be more fun than what's happening now, which is that I make him ask for sex, and he has to push for the way he wants sex to happen.
- I'm failing to get the real point, which is that he doesn't feel *loved* by me. I'm treating him like he's some kind of sex monster, when what he really wants is to feel like I really care about him. I also get angry at him all the time and criticize him and get impatient with him, and in all those ways I show him I don't care about him. Not having sex with him just adds to his feeling of not being loved by me.

You'll be sharing this assignment with your partner tomorrow, on Day Nineteen.

Fifth Assignment

In the following space describe two issues or situations where you believe your partner has not listened well to you.

You'll be sharing this assignment with your partner tomorrow, on Day Nineteen.

Sixth Assignment

Share your Third and Fourth Assignments with a friend, and in the space below describe this experience.

DAY NINETEEN:
Loving Acts—
Looking, Touching, Talking

First Assignment

Share with your partner what you wrote for your Third and Fourth Assignments from Day Eighteen. As you complete these assignments, you'll both have opportunities to hear your partner listen with new skills and openness. This can be a great experience. If your partner doesn't demonstrate listening to the degree of sensitivity that you might like, relax. Learning to genuinely listen requires a great deal of time, effort, and experience.

Second Assignment

Share with your partner what you wrote for your Fifth Assignment from Day Eighteen. This is a potentially volatile assignment for both of you. First, as your partner describes to you situations where you have not listened well to him or her, you might well feel an inclination to defend yourself. Do not give in to this temptation. This is your opportunity to practice in person what you did in the Fourth Assignment of Day Eighteen, using the principles of the 3 x 5 card. In fact, you can apply principles here in person—like "Ask questions"—that you couldn't do in writing. Make use of this wonderful opportunity to learn the skill of genuine listening. The listening mistakes you have made in the past are unimportant. What matters is what you're learning.

Second, as you begin to describe to your partner situations where he or she has not listened well to you, you might feel compelled to vent the frustrations of many years. Do not give in to this temptation either. Do not force your partner to instantly make up for your long term feelings of being unseen, unappreciated, and alone. Allow him or her to *gradually* enjoy the process of learning to listen, which is the only way this process can happen successfully.

Third Assignment

In the meeting, read from the book *Real Love in Marriage*:
Begin   Page 95, Title: Look
End   Page 98, Title: Say "I Love You"

(Complete the following assignments outside the meeting.)

Fourth Assignment

In the space below write the questions you'll be asking your partner tomorrow—on Day Twenty—about the degree of eye contact in your relationship. Allow me to offer some suggestions:

- When I'm talking to you, do I look directly into your eyes enough?
- When I'm not talking to you, do I look directly into your eyes enough?
- If the answer to either of these questions is *no*, has that bothered you?

You'll be sharing this assignment with your partner tomorrow, on Day Twenty.

Fifth Assignment

In the space below describe:

    A. Some of the *non-sexual* ways you would like to be touched by your partner. How often? When? Where? For how long? You might use the list on page 96 of *Real Love in Marriage* as a guide.

    B. What are some of the ways you would like to begin touching your partner to communicate your unconditional love for him or her?

You'll be sharing this assignment with your partner tomorrow, on Day Twenty.

Sixth Assignment

In my experience with a great many couples, consistently talking together is the single activity that has proven to create and maintain Real Love better than all others, and of all forms of talking, it's telling the truth about ourselves that has proven to be most productive. Considering the power of this activity, why leave it to random encounters? If we want anything else in life to increase steadily—in business or athletics, for example—we *schedule* it, often and regularly. We would be wise to do this scheduling with any positive characteristic that we wished to increase in our marriages, and I recommend this with truth telling.

I suggest that you commit yourself to *daily* meetings with your partner, in which you spend at least fifteen minutes, including the following activities:

- Read a book that includes principles that will contribute to the philosophical, spiritual, or emotional foundation of your relationship. This might include *Real Love in Marriage*, scriptures (Bible, the Qur'ân, or other sacred texts), or other uplifting books.
- Go through the 40-day program of this workbook more than once.
- Bring up any Getting and Protecting Behaviors that you have used during the day. Such spontaneous acts of truth telling have enormously healing effects in a marriage.
- Ask the question, "Is there anything that happened in the past day that we wish had gone differently?" This gives both of you the opportunity to describe incidents that may have caused conflict. Never allow conflicts to build up in a marriage. Take care of them while they are small, rather than allowing them to build to the volcanic stage. We'll be talking more about conflicts later in the workbook.
- Schedule time together for activities: walks, vacations, weekends, dates, and so on.
- Go over schedules, to be certain that you're avoiding potential conflicts. If this is done on a daily basis, it's much easier to avoid problems.

Review your willingness to have these meetings daily. In the space below describe what you'd like to see happen in these meetings. Then be prepared to talk with your partner tomorrow—on Day Twenty—about scheduling these meetings every day. These meetings can make the difference between success and failure in a marriage.

DAY TWENTY:
Loving Acts—
Random Acts of Kindness

First Assignment

Share with your partner what you wrote for your Fourth Assignment from Day Nineteen. Be careful here. As you tell your partner what degree of eye contact you'd like, you are not delivering an order, as you might at a fast food restaurant. As you share this assignment, both of you need to remember that you're just gathering information about your partner. You're learning what your partner would prefer, and over time it is hoped that this information will gradually influence your behavior. This assignment is not meant to *obligate* either of you to any pattern of behavior.

If your partner says you don't look at him or her as much as he or she would like, I suggest that you not make a commitment about this behavior, because if you fail to keep your commitment—which is likely—this may lead to feelings of discouragement on your part or irritation on his or her part. Just use your partner's answers in this assignment as information to guide your future behavior.

Second Assignment

Review the Fifth Assignment from Day Nineteen. Again, both of you need to remember here that you're just gathering information about your partner. You're each *learning* potential ways that might contribute to your partner feeling more loved. This is *not* an opportunity to obligate your partner to begin touching you—and thereby demonstrate love for you—in a particular way. If you misuse this assignment in this way—if you lean on your partner to begin demonstrating love for you in the ways you desire—you will only create bad feelings. Even if you get the touching you're looking for, if it's a result of manipulation or pressure on your part, you won't feel like it's being given to you *unconditionally*, which is a requirement of Real Love.

Third Assignment

Review the Fifth Assignment from Day Nineteen. Determine whether you are willing to make a commitment to meet together to accomplish all or some of the goals listed in that assignment. You may have noticed that in the process of holding your meetings to accomplish the 40-day program of this workbook, you've already been fulfilling much of the description of these daily couple's meetings—reading and truth telling, for example—so making a commitment to hold daily meetings as a couple would only be a continuation of what you've been doing for the workbook.

Many families have hectic, ever-changing schedules. For that reason it may not be possible to set your couple's meeting for the same time every day. You could, however, commit that at the end of each meeting you will set the time of the next day's meeting.

Fourth Assignment

In the meeting, read from the book *Real Love in Marriage*:
Begin   Page 98, Title: Say "I Love You"
End   Page 100, bottom of page

(Complete the following assignments outside the meeting.)

Fifth Assignment

In the following space write ten or more loving acts that you would be willing to demonstrate toward your partner. Pages 98-100 above give you some examples that might get your creative juices flowing.

You'll be sharing this assignment with your partner tomorrow, on Day Twenty-One.

Sixth Assignment

Make a commitment to yourself that every day you will share with your partner at least one of the loving acts you have written above. Moreover, if you keep a written record of your behavior, you'll discover that you'll be prompted to be more consistent in your performance. For that reason, commit to obtain a calendar or schedule book or journal—if you don't already have one—and note every day the loving acts you share with your partner. *Do not*, however, under any conditions, ever show this calendar to your partner, since the likelihood would be high that you would be doing this to provoke feelings of praise or gratitude in your partner. This, of course, would ruin the entire motivation of your offering *unconditionally* loving acts.

I also suggest that over time you add to the list you made in the Fifth Assignment.

Seventh Assignment

In the space below write ten or more loving acts that you would like your partner to demonstrate toward you.

You'll be sharing this assignment with your partner tomorrow, on Day Twenty-One.

DAY TWENTY-ONE:
Loving Acts—More Loving

First Assignment

Review the Seventh Assignment from Day Twenty. This is a wonderful opportunity for both of you to learn what the other person would enjoy as tokens of love in your relationship, but you must also be very careful here. As you present your partner with some of your desires for loving acts, there could be a strong temptation—especially if you have not been sufficiently filled with Real Love—for you to unconsciously turn your list of desires into a list of expectations and demands, with all the usual attendant problems: Your partner will tend to feel burdened, frightened, and probably irritated by your expectations; and your expectations will virtually guarantee disappointment and irritation for you.

In this assignment, both of you are giving each other several possible steps on a roadmap to achieve a higher level of sharing and compassion between you. You are not obligated to take any of these steps—in some cases you may not be *able* to fill your partner's requests—but with these lists you are learning additional paths that you may have been previously unaware of.

Second Assignment

In the meeting, read from the book *Real Love in Marriage*:
Begin   Page 101, Title: Cooperate
End   Page 107, Title: Exercises

(Complete the following assignments outside the meeting.)

Third Assignment

Make a commitment to yourself that sometime in the next twenty-four hours you will in some way inquire about the welfare of your partner. Following are some examples of what you might say:

- Touch him or her on the arm, look him or her in the eye, and say, "How are you feeling?" This is quite different from the usual, superficial social greeting that we hear every day.
- "Is there anything you want to talk about?" Don't ask this question when your partner is obviously busy with something else.
- "You look like you have something on your mind. I'd love to hear what it is."
- "How did your day go?" Don't ask this in passing. Make it clear that you're really interested. Sit down, look him or her in the eye, and make it obvious that you have nothing else to do but listen.

Repeat this task—this asking your partner about his or her welfare—on a regular basis. We tend not to accomplish such things on a regular basis unless we schedule them, so I suggest the following: On the calendar or other scheduling device that I mentioned in the Sixth Assignment of Day Twenty, write the word ASK on a day of your choosing—Tuesday, for example—for every week for the remainder of the year. This will remind you to accomplish this loving act at least once a week.

Fourth Assignment

The one day that most men dislike more than any other is Valentine's Day. Why? A single word: expectations, which are discussed on pages 46-49 of *Real Love in Marriage*. Men know that their loved ones have enormous expectations of them, and that makes the gift giving associated with Valentine's Day no fun at all. If a man doesn't get the right gift, he's doomed. If he does, he succeeds only in avoiding disapproval. Even women don't end up enjoying Valentine's Day all that much. First, they stew and fuss in their expectations, worrying that they won't receive what they want. They ruin the day before it even arrives. And then, if they don't get what they expected, they're irritated at their partner, destroying the day for both of them. Even if such women do get what they expected, they don't feel genuinely loved, because Real Love is possible only if a gift is given freely, without expectations.

The moral of this tale is that a gift has the greatest impact when it's given for no reason at all. If someone gives you a gift not because it's your birthday, not because it's Valentine's day, not because you asked them to, but only because he or she *wants* to—because he or she is genuinely concerned for your happiness—that act has the potential of producing a wonderful feeling in you.

For that reason I suggest that you make a commitment here that you will stop what you are doing, find your partner, and indicate to your partner in some way that you were thinking about him or her, or that you simply wanted to be with him or her. Because many of us have done this rarely—or none at all—allow me to offer some suggestions about what you might do or say on these occasions:

- Throw your arms around her and say, "Where have you been? I haven't seen you in seventeen minutes!"
- Simply touch his shoulder while he's working and say, "I was thinking about you."
- Touch her shoulder and ask, "You doing all right?"
- Sit down next to him—very close—while he's watching television, and touch his leg. Say, "I just came to spend a few seconds with you. I'm not trying to interrupt what you're doing." This will work most effectively if you do this during a commercial or a time when he won't feel interrupted.
- Put your arms around her. Put your nose right up to her nose. Look her in the eyes. Do this slowly. Say, "I was missing you."

On some days you might want to find your partner like this several times in a single day. People really like to be wanted, and that is what you're communicating by finding your partner.

Love is most effectively communicated when it is done regularly, so I highly recommend that this assignment be calendared, as you will be doing for the Third Assignment above and for the Sixth Assignment of Day Twenty. Make a commitment to yourself that you will find your partner and indicate some measure of unsolicited affection at least four times a week. This commitment will take mere moments from your day, and you will be surprised at the ample rewards that you will enjoy.

Fifth Assignment

We all have resentments about how our partners have treated us in the past. In the space below describe at least two behaviors or events for which you still have resentful feelings toward your partner.

In the following space, make a written commitment right now that you will let go of one of these resentments. Completely. That you will never bring it up again. That you will never hold this event or behavior against your partner again. This is more important than I can possibly emphasize.

Imagine that you're going on a fifty-mile hike in the mountains. You'll be carrying a heavy backpack, and the journey will be grueling. Given the choice, how big a pebble would you like to have in your boot as you walk? 1/4 inch? 1/8 inch? 1/16 inch? Or would you choose to have no pebble at all in your boot to rub against the skin of your foot, causing blisters, infections, and other injuries? The answer is obvious, isn't it? Over a fifty-mile journey, even the smallest pebble could lead to crippling injury, and the same is true with resentments in relationships. We simply can't afford them—any of them.

You cannot simultaneously resent your partner and unconditionally love him or her. It's impossible, so it's critical that you lay aside all resentments, irritations, grudges, and so on. But many of us have tried for all our lives to eliminate such resentments, without success, so how can we accomplish this difficult task? We have already introduced the tools needed for this:

- Understanding your partner. When you realize that your partner's unproductive behaviors really are reactions to emptiness and fear—that your partner truly is drowning when he or she is behaving badly—it becomes impossible for you to remain irritated or resentful at your partner when he or she behaves badly.
- Getting out of the pool yourself. As you tell the truth about yourself to others, you create opportunities to find the Real Love (Truth → Seen → Accepted → Loved) that will naturally eliminate anger and resentment in your life. Anger is a reaction to emptiness and fear, so when you feel enough Real Love, your anger naturally disappears.
- Understanding your own resentment. In Chapters One and Two of *Real Love in Marriage* we discussed how Getting and Protecting Behaviors—including resentment and anger—have a uniformly destructive effect on everyone. Anger is unloving and selfish. When I'm angry, I can never be happy, and I have a negative effect on everyone around me. For that reason alone, no matter what my partner has done, if I am angry and resentful, I am wrong. To be sure, in that moment my partner may also be wrong, but *if I am angry, I am wrong.* If I can remember that, it becomes much more difficult for me to self-righteously hang on to my resentments.

I encourage you to understand that you are not making a choice to let go of this resentment toward your partner as a favor to him or

her. You're doing it simply because anger *doesn't work*, because it's
selfish, because it never leads to happiness, and because it's therefore
foolish. You want to let go of all the resentments in your life because
you want to be happy.

You'll be sharing this assignment and this commitment with your
partner tomorrow, on Day Twenty-Two.

DAY TWENTY-TWO:
Conflict—
It's Always About Real Love

First Assignment

Review both parts of the Fifth Assignment from Day Twenty-One, but only if you have made a commitment to actually *let go* of a resentment. Forgiveness is a very sweet moment in a relationship. Savor this. Create more of these moments. Come back to the Fifth Assignment regularly.

Second Assignment

In the meeting, read from the book *Real Love in Marriage*:
Begin   Page 110, Title: The Great Wars
End   Page 116, Title: Listen

(Complete the following assignments outside the meeting.)

Third Assignment

We get so distracted by the *words* used in conversations, especially in conflicts. Let's imagine, for example, that you're backing your car out of the driveway, and you drive it over my foot. If I angrily shout, "You are so stupid," the likelihood is very strong that you will focus on two words in that sentence: *you* and *stupid*. And you will do so because both words are highly emotionally charged. We're all rather attached to the word *you*—when it applies to us, that is—and the word *stupid* tends to provoke an emotional response in almost everyone.

Your tendency to focus on the words *you* and *stupid* will naturally lead you to feel a bit defensive, after which you will probably feel an inclination to respond by justifying yourself. You may explain that you didn't see me, or you may describe the terribly urgent mission that prompted you to back the car out of the driveway, or you may actually criticize *me* for being in *your driveway* and getting in your way. Of course at that point I would be further enraged at your attempts to defend yourself, and our conflict could only escalate.

How many conflicts have followed a course very much like this? I don't hesitate to say that *most* conflicts follow such a pattern, where the participants unwittingly fail to identify the core issue and become distracted instead by the details or the words of the moment. You, however, are about to break that pattern, and the beginning of this wisdom is easy to explain.

What people need most is Real Love, and when they don't have enough of it, they demonstrate their emptiness and fear in a variety of ways. In fact, I would go so far as to say that whenever people become "upset" in a conversation—anxious, angry, irritated, annoyed, frustrated, unusually animated, and so on—they are demonstrating a lack of Real Love. In short, *When people become upset in an interaction, the subject of the conversation is Real Love*, and if we don't understand this, we will find the interaction or conversation enormously frustrating, if not impossibly difficult.

In the following space describe an issue about which you and your partner keep having conflicts. Then describe how your understanding of the above paragraphs and of pages 110-116 of *Real Love in Marriage* helps you change the way you see the conflict, as well as how you will change the way you approach the conflict the next time it presents itself.

Allow me to provide a couple of abbreviated examples of this assignment:

- My husband and I have quarreled over money for as long as I can remember. Mostly he tells me that I'm not responsible about how I spend it, and then I show him that everything I buy is necessary. But when I bring out the receipts, he just gets angrier, and then he brings out more accusations, and eventually he can show me how I've spent money on something that might not have been an absolutely necessity. I mean, come on, it's not like I've never made a frivolous purchase in our lives.

But now I'm getting the real point of these arguments. He's never felt unconditionally loved, so he's empty and afraid all the time, and he worries about things like finances a lot. When he gets nervous, about our finances, sometimes he just needs somebody to blame, so he turns to me. The moment I defend myself—even though I might technically be *right* about what I'm saying—he can feel that my focus is on *myself*, and that's the beginning of the end, because in the moment he is empty and afraid what he really needs most is for me to simply love him. The financial stuff is all secondary. The second he gets anxious, the subject of the conversation is *not money, it's love*. I have to remember that and pay more attention to loving him.

- For years my wife has been telling me that I don't help enough around the house with the kids, and then I get offended. I tell her that I do help, and I point out the times that I *have* helped. Of course, then if I'm in a bad mood, sometimes I'll tell her, "And why would I want to help you do *anything*, when you talk to me like this? In fact, why would *anybody* want to be around you when you're like this?" Naturally, that doesn't go over very well, and then our conversation goes down the drain pretty fast. She is certain that she's right, and I'm positive that I'm right. We both start yelling, and after a while I just withdraw and start drinking.

  Until now I never understood what the real subject of the conversation was all along. All Connie ever wanted to know was this: "Do you love me, and do you love me enough to help me with the kids when I'm tired and when you're tired?" My mistake was always that I misunderstood the subject of the conversation. I had it all wrong. I thought the details mattered. I thought I was being asked, "Had I ever helped in the past?" Or "Was I a good father, and could I prove that with the time I'd put in helping with the kids?" So, because I thought those were the subjects of the conversation, I got all distracted and devoted myself to proving that I was *right*, but all she wanted to know was that I loved her. The real subject of the conversation was *love*, and I missed it. I needed to shut up, quit being angry, and love her.

You'll be sharing this assignment with your partner tomorrow, on Day Twenty-Three.

Fourth Assignment

Share your Third Assignment with a friend, and in the space below describe this experience.

Fifth Assignment

In the Fifth and Sixth Assignments of Day Twenty, you committed to create a list of loving acts, at least one of which you would demonstrate toward your partner. You also committed to calendar these acts. In the space below, describe the results of this effort. Are you keeping your commitment? As a result of your loving acts, are you feeling an increased connection with your partner? Are you feeling happier yourself? Are you seeing any change in your relationship? (Keep in mind, however, that you don't want to initiate any "loving act" *so that* your partner will react in any particular way, or your motivation wouldn't be *unconditional*.)

DAY TWENTY-THREE:
Conflict—Listen

First Assignment

Review the Third Assignment from Day Twenty-Two. A word of caution here: Do not use this opportunity to make an attempt to entirely resolve the conflict you've addressed in this assignment. Remember that the goal of this assignment was only to demonstrate how a conflict might be affected by understanding that the root of a conflict is "always about Real Love," not about the words and the details involved.

In short, this assignment is intended to create nothing but positive feelings. If you experience any frustration, irritation or the like, you're demonstrating that you simply do not yet have the tools required to resolve this conflict in a loving way. Don't feel bad about it, but don't keep talking and trying to resolve the conflict with old and unproductive tools either. Instead, make a commitment to continue the learning process of the 40 days—and particularly this section on the elimination of conflict—and learn how to respond to your partner in much more loving ways, regardless of the stress of the circumstances.

Second Assignment

In the meeting, read from the book *Real Love in Marriage*:
Begin   Page 116, Title: Listen
End   Page 123, Title: Never Speak in Anger

(Complete the following assignments outside the meeting.)

Third Assignment

In the Third Assignment of Day Twenty-Two you described a conflict that you and your partner keep repeating in your relationship. Now—in the following space—describe how the First and Second Rules of Seeing help you change the way you see this conflict, as well as how you might change the way you will approach the conflict the next time it presents itself.

Allow me to provide an example of this assignment, using a conflict I suggested from Day Twenty-Two:

> For years my wife has been telling me that I don't help enough around the house with the kids, and in the process of defending myself I almost always point out something *she* isn't doing for me around the house. Now, what I point out to her happens to be *true*, but I'm *wrong* to bring it up when I do. I need to remember that in any given conversation, all that really matters is whether we increase the Real Love in our relationship, and when I change the subject when she's talking, what I communicate to her is that I don't love her. The First Rule of Seeing helps me to be more loving by reminding me that there can only be one person speaking at a time, and the Second Rule makes it easy to determine who the Speaker is. When my partner brings up the subject of my not helping the kids, *that* is the subject we're talking about, and I need to listen until she feels heard and loved. *That* is the point I've been missing.

You'll be sharing this assignment with your partner tomorrow, on Day Twenty-Four.

Fourth Assignment

The Third Rule of Seeing gives us a profound insight into what people are really saying most of the time they speak. The moment people become anxious, frustrated, angry, or afraid, they begin to describe their own need for Real Love—*regardless of the words they might be using at the time*. A drowning man, for example, might scream at you that *you* are not helping him fast enough, or that you are helping him too roughly, or whatever. But what he's really describing is his own desperation for air. As we discussed in the metaphor of the two dollars—pages 37-38 of *Real Love in Marriage*—if we become angry at the theft of two dollars, we're describing not the act of another person but our own financial condition.

Similarly, when people are emotionally empty—when they're afraid and angry, for example—they may use words that describe the flaws of other people, but their primary concern is for *their own* emptiness, and their words flow from that concern. Nearly all their words are really a description of *themselves*.

In the space below apply your understanding of The Third Rule of Seeing to the conflict you described in the Third Assignment. Following is an example of this assignment, using the conflict I provided in the Third Assignment:

> For years my wife has been telling me that I don't help enough around the house with the kids, and I've always defended myself vigorously, because she has been so critical of me. She tells me—directly and indirectly—that I'm lazy and irresponsible, and I just can't stand to hear those accusations, so I get defensive, and then the fight is on. Now I'm understanding that all this time she's really been describing *herself*, not me. All this time I could only hear her accusations of *me*, but what she's really been saying is this: "*I* don't feel loved by you. When you don't help me with the kids, I feel like you don't care about *me*." What I've been missing is that she's really been saying, "Please love me." If I'd heard that message from the beginning, we could have eliminated a lot of conflict.

You'll be sharing this assignment with your partner tomorrow, on Day Twenty-Four.

Fifth Assignment

The Fourth Rule of Seeing boils down to this: In a given interaction with your partner, if you can't be loving, find someone who can give you the Real Love you need so you can bring that back to your partner, so you can continue a loving interaction.

In the following space, apply that wisdom to the conflict that you have been describing in the Third and Fourth Assignments. Following is an example of this assignment, using the conflict I provided in the Third Assignment:

> For years my wife has been telling me that I don't help enough around the house with the kids, and then I defend myself, and the conflict predictably goes crazy. Of course what I never understood was that we've *both* been empty and afraid, and then when we exchange Getting and Protecting Behaviors we couldn't possibly have a loving or productive interaction. We were both drowning, and two drowning people can only make things worse for each other. So now when I begin to feel threatened, I need to remember that I just have no love to give my partner and that I can find other sources of Real Love—wise men and women—so I can then be more loving and productive in my interactions with my partner. I've always thought I had to defend myself, but I don't. I can get love from wise men and women instead.

You'll be sharing this assignment with your partner tomorrow, on Day Twenty-Four.

Sixth Assignment

Share your Third, Fourth, and Fifth Assignments with a wise friend, and in the space below describe this experience.

DAY TWENTY-FOUR:
Conflict—No Anger

First Assignment

Review the Third, Fourth, and Fifth Assignments from Day Twenty-Three. This sharing does not commit you to anything with your partner. You're just sharing with him or her what you're learning. This is a vulnerable, open act on your part and tends to lead to a building of mutual trust.

Second Assignment

In the meeting, read from the book *Real Love in Marriage*:
Begin   Page 123, Title: Never Speak in Anger
End   Page 129, Title: Tell the Truth about Yourself

(Complete the following assignments outside the meeting.)

Third Assignment

In the following space describe a recent conflict where you became angry. Now describe how you could have handled the conflict differently using the five steps described on pages 123-129 of *Real Love in Marriage*.

You'll be sharing this assignment with your partner tomorrow, on Day Twenty-Five.

Fourth Assignment

Share your Third Assignment with a wise friend, and in the space below describe this experience.

Fifth Assignment

In the Fifth and Sixth Assignments of Day Twenty, you committed to create a list of loving acts, at least one of which you would demonstrate toward your partner. You also committed to calendar these acts. In the space below, describe the results of this effort. Are you keeping your commitment? As a result of your loving acts, are you feeling an increased connection with your partner? Are you feeling happier yourself? Are you seeing any change in your relationship? (Keep in mind, however, that you don't want to initiate any "loving act" *so that* your partner will react in any particular way, or your motivation wouldn't be *unconditional*.)

DAY TWENTY-FIVE:
Conflict—Telling the Truth

First Assignment

Review the Third Assignment from Day Twenty-Four with your partner. What did you learn together as you discussed this assignment?

Second Assignment

In the meeting, read from the book *Real Love in Marriage*:
Begin   Page 129, Title: Tell the Truth about Yourself
End   Page 138, Title: Recognize What You Really Want

(Complete the following assignments outside the meeting.)

Third Assignment

The above nine pages could be distilled into a single sentence: "When in doubt in a conflict, tell the truth about yourself." In the following space, apply this guideline to the conflict you have already described on Days Twenty-Two and Twenty-Three. Or you could apply this guideline to a new conflict. Allow me to illustrate by applying truth telling to the conflicts I've been using:

- My husband and I have quarreled over money for as long as I can remember. When he tells me how I'm not responsible about spending, I get angry and defend myself, and we fall into a cycle of Protecting Behaviors. But I can see an easy way out of this. All I have to do is tell the truth. I could tell the truth about the occasions when I have *not* been responsible and simply not defend myself about the rest. It's not worth it. I could even thank him for pointing out the irresponsible occasions and offer to do a better job of reporting my spending—like turning in receipts and stuff. He'd love that, and there would be no conflict at all. And, most important, he'd feel like I was listening to him and caring about him. I should have caught on to this a long time ago.

- For years my wife has been telling me that I don't help enough around the house with the kids, and then I get offended and fight back with my own arguments. It would be so much simpler—and more loving—if I just told the truth. The truth is, even though I sometimes help around the house, she's *right*. A lot of the time, when she needs me most, I hide out and make excuses for why I can't help her. Sometimes I act like they aren't even my kids, which is embarrassing. I just need to admit the truth about that—that I've been selfish and lazy—and give her the opportunity to accept and love me for who I really am, flaws and all. It's got to be better than what we have now, right? Sometimes I could also tell the truth about myself to my friend Mark, or just to myself.

You'll be sharing this assignment with your partner tomorrow, on Day Twenty-Six.

Fourth Assignment

Share your Assignment with a wise friend, and in the space below describe this experience.

DAY TWENTY-SIX:
Conflict—
Working Out What Matters

First Assignment

Review your Third Assignment from Day Twenty-Five with your partner.

Second Assignment

In the meeting, read from the book *Real Love in Marriage*:
Begin   Page 138, Title: Recognize What You Really Want
End   Page 147, Title: Refuse to Be in Conflict

(Complete the following assignments outside the meeting.)

Third Assignment

In the following space, discuss a conflict that you and your partner have been experiencing between you, preferably one you have not used for discussion thus far. Use the tools you have acquired over the previous several Days of the workbook and on pages 138-147 of *Real Love in Marriage* to discuss how you will resolve this conflict. You will

- remember that it's always about Real Love.
- listen, using the Four Rules of Seeing.
- not speak in anger.
- tell the truth about yourself.
- remember what you really want in your relationship, which is an increase in Real Love—not to be right or to accomplish any particular task.

Tomorrow, on Day Twenty-Seven, you will use this outline to actually resolve this conflict with your partner.

Fourth Assignment

Share your Assignment with a wise friend, and in the space below describe this experience.

Fifth Assignment

In the Fourth Assignment of Day Twenty-One, you committed to find your partner and indicate some measure of unsolicited affection at least four times a week, and to calendar this activity, probably using the same calendar as for the Sixth Assignment of Day Twenty. In the space below, describe the results of this effort. Are you keeping your commitment? As a result of your loving acts, are you feeling an increased connection with your partner? Are you feeling happier yourself? Are you seeing any change in your relationship?

DAY TWENTY-SEVEN:
Conflict—
Refusing to Be in It

First Assignment

Review your Third Assignment from Day Twenty-Six with your partner. You have an opportunity here to work out a conflict using a great many more tools than you had only a month ago. Be patient and allow true principles and the power of Real Love to help you.

Second Assignment

In the meeting, read from the book *Real Love in Marriage*:
Begin   Page 147, Title: Refuse to Be in Conflict
End   Page 152, Title: Preventing Conflict

(Complete the following assignments outside the meeting.)

Third Assignment

It is never wise to continue in a conversation that we know will not be loving. For that reason, we need to be prepared to free ourselves from situations where conflict is building. Using the examples on pages 148-149 of *Real Love in Marriage* as a model, use the following space to create your own words that you can use to remove you from the bondage of potential conflict.

You'll be sharing this assignment with your partner tomorrow, on Day Twenty-Eight.

Fourth Assignment

Let's get practical here. Sometimes when you get into an argument, you develop an irresistible urge to finish it. It becomes almost a blood lust. You want to get your point across, no matter what the cost. Picture yourself in that situation: Your temper is up, you are determined to make your partner listen to something you want to say, but he or she isn't quite listening. Now, in the following space, write the words and behavior that you would like to hear and see from your partner that would be most helpful in stopping this conflict.

Again, you have the examples on pages 148-149 of *Real Love in Marriage* to spur your creativity, but allow me to provide a couple more:

- When your partner sees that you're irritated, she walks up to you, puts her arms around you, and buries her head in your chest. After a few seconds, she looks into your face and says, "I understand what you're saying, and I know you've been trying to communicate this to me before. I'm sorry that I've been slow about hearing it. This conversation is too important to be affected by my not listening well, and I believe I'll be in a better place to listen to you later this afternoon. So would you be willing to continue this conversation then?"
- When your partner sees your frustration, he sits down next to you on the coach, takes both your hands in his hands, looks you in the eye, and says, "I *need* to listen to every word you're saying, I *want* to listen to what you're saying, and I know that I *haven't* been listening, or you wouldn't be frustrated right now. So rather than continue with what I'm doing—which isn't working—let me propose that we take a break. Let me gather my thoughts and come back when I'm listening to you better. How about two hours? Would that be all right?

You'll be sharing this assignment with your partner tomorrow, on Day Twenty-Eight.

Fifth Assignment

In the Fifth Assignment of Day Twenty-One, you made a commitment that you would let go of a resentment that you held toward your partner, using the tools described in that assignment. How are you doing with that assignment? Have you managed to let go of that resentment completely? If not, are you continuing to work on it? Are you willing to? If you have let go of the resentment, how does it feel? Can you feel in the increase in the power of Real Love between you as you have removed this obstacle? Are you willing to choose another resentment and let it go?

DAY TWENTY-EIGHT:
Conflict—Preventing It

First Assignment

Share your Third and Fourth Assignments from Day Twenty-Seven with your partner. Most of you will immediately notice that the outcomes of the Third and Fourth Assignments are quite different. Most people tend to come up with somewhat defensive words for the Third Assignment, because they are thinking of words to stop a conflict where they are being attacked.

On the other hand, people usually offer more sensitive words and behaviors for the Fourth Assignment, because in this case *they* are the angry and attacking party, so they are in need of compassion and understanding.

As you share your assignments with each other, *agree* on the words and behavior that each of you could *receive* that would be sufficient to stop a conflict. You'll discover that this will be very close to what each of you has already written as your Fourth Assignment for Day Twenty-Seven. You'll also discover how wise it is for you to agree on this conflict-stopping pattern now, while you are having a calm discussion. It's like having a disaster preparation plan in place *before* the disaster, rather than trying to come up with one in the heat of the moment, which is rarely as effective.

Second Assignment

In the meeting, read from the book *Real Love in Marriage*:
Begin   Page 152, Title: Preventing Conflict
End   Page 156, Title: Offer Unsolicited Love

(Complete the following assignments outside the meeting.)

Third Assignment

We cause so many unnecessary conflicts in our marriages by criticizing our partners over matters that could best be ignored. In the following space choose at least two issues about which you have criticized your partner, causing any tension in your relationship. Using the four guiding questions on pages 153-154 in *Real Love in Marriage*, examine how you might see this issue differently. Until we can answer all four questions with a resounding *Yes*, the damage we cause to our relationships by addressing any specific issue far outweighs any benefit we might accomplish.

Allow me to illustrate the fulfillment of this assignment by providing a couple of examples:

First Example: The Toilet Seat. I am so tired of him not putting the toilet seat back down when he's finished in the bathroom. I've talked to him about it a thousand times, but all it does is cause fights between us.

- Is this any of my business?
  When the toilet seat is up, it does inconvenience me, so yes, it is my business.
- Does this really matter?
  It takes me maybe one to two seconds to put the toilet seat down, so is this a *significant* issue for me to fuss at him about? Is this worth me poisoning our relationship about, which is what I've been doing to this point? *No*, probably not.
- Am I being unconditionally loving?
  Not even close. Every time I approach this issue, I'm filled with expectations, demands, irritation, and more. I'm far from loving, and he can feel that. This issue causes nothing but bad feelings.
- Is he or she capable of hearing what I'm about to say?
  This has been a touchy subject from the beginning, and I know that, so there's no way I can bring it up in a way that he can hear it.

Bottom line: I thought it was important that I got my way about this, that he put that darned toilet seat down, but I can see now that the overall damage has been far greater than any good that I could ever get from the seat being put down. I've been ridiculous to insist on this. And if I were really being truthful here, do ever put the toilet seat *up* for him after I'm done in the bathroom? No, so I have a bit of re-examination to do here.

Second Example: Parking the Car. I've told her a hundred times how to park her car in the garage. I've showed her how to do it too. But she keeps parking it too close to my car, so I can't get into it or out of it, or she parks too close to the wall, and then I can't get stuff out of the cabinets that are on that wall. A couple of times she has actually scraped the cabinets. Once she tore the mirror off the driver's side. What's it going to take for her to get this?

- Is this any of my business?
  Sure it's my business. When she does it wrong, I can hardly get it my car, or I can't get into my garage cabinets. Or I have to fix the car when she wrecks it.
- Does this really matter?
  I'm not as sure about this one. I don't want this to hurt our relationship, but I also don't want to keep spending money on fixing the car, and I don't want to keep having to squeeze into my car. To be honest, though, the total cost of fixing the car over the years has been pretty small, and I'd be glad to pay that if our marriage were happier. And if we were happier, squeezing into a small space to get into my car every once in a while would be an insignificant thing. So, I guess this doesn't really matter that much. I've just *let* it bother me.
- Am I being unconditionally loving?
  No, I'm really not. Whenever I bring this up, I'm critical, impatient, and angry. I make her feel bad, and I affect our marriage in awful ways.
- Is he or she capable of hearing what I'm about to say?
  No way. After all the terrible things I've said on this subject, I've created an open wound so that she can't hear a single thing I have to say about this.

Bottom line: I've created terrible feelings between my wife and me about her parking the car, and even if she were parking the car perfectly now as a result of what I've said, it wouldn't be worth it. If she were parking the car perfectly, I'd only be saving a few dollars and a few moments of convenience. The price I've been paying—a miserable partner, an angry relationship, and me being unhappy—has been far too high.

You'll be sharing this assignment with your partner tomorrow, on Day Twenty-Nine.

Fourth Assignment

Share your Assignment with a wise friend, and in the space below describe this experience.

Fifth Assignment

In the Fifth and Sixth Assignments of Day Twenty, you committed to create a list of loving acts, at least one of which you would demonstrate toward your partner. You also committed to calendar these acts. In the space below, describe the results of this effort. Are you keeping your commitment? As a result of your loving acts, are you feeling an increased connection with your partner? Are you feeling happier yourself? Are you seeing any change in your relationship?

DAY TWENTY-NINE:
Conflict—Loving Acts

First Assignment

Share your Third Assignment from Day Twenty-Eight with your partner. This is a great opportunity for both of you to demonstrate what you've learned about staying out of each other's business. As your partner shares this assignment with you, however, do not take this opportunity to amplify his or he mistakes. If he or she talks about being too critical of you about some issue, for example, do not succumb to the temptation to say something like, "Yes, you sure have been critical. Not only that, but you have also . . ." Our partners will find it much more difficult to continue telling us the truth about themselves if we make that process unpleasant.

Second Assignment

In the meeting, read from the book *Real Love in Marriage*:
Begin   Page 156, Title: Offer Unsolicited Love
End   Page 160, Title: Making the Primary Decision . . .

Third Assignment

It is unspeakably important that in your relationship an open discussion about issues be maintained, so that no tension builds that would detract from the Real Love between you. Toward that end, review the commitment you made in the Sixth Assignment of Day Nineteen to meet daily with your partner to discuss any potential sources of conflict between you, among other agenda items.

At this point consider making a commitment with your partner to spend at least two uninterrupted hours with him or her on a "date," where you will have even more opportunities to enrich your relationship by discussion of issues that might interfere in any way with the Real Love between you. It's also a great opportunity just to have fun together.

(Complete the following assignments outside the meeting.)

Fourth Assignment

It is often the case that when we feel most in need of attention we feel least like communicating our needs. On these occasions we may need our partners to help us communicate what we need. Page 157 of *Real Love in Marriage* suggests a general, four-step approach to helping someone identify their needs. Imagine that *you* are the person who is feeling needy and non-communicative, and your partner is trying to help you, using this four-step approach. Now, in this moment that you are feeling more communicative, use the following space to make some suggestions that might help your partner to communicate with you on an occasion when he or she might use these four steps. The purpose of this assignment is to give your partner the language that will seem least intrusive, least bothersome, and most productive to you at a time when you will be non-communicative and more prone to being argumentative.

Allow me to provide an example of *your* completing this assignment, with *you* speaking in the first person directly to your partner:

- Ask general questions.
  If I'm acting withdrawn, don't make a big deal about it. Don't act like you're trying to "fix" me or "pull me out of it." Just say, "Is everything all right?"
- Ask specific questions.
  If the general questions don't work, you might try some of these questions:
  "Is there anything going on at work that's bothering you?"
  "Sometimes I do or say something that bothers you, and I don't realize I've done it. Then there's no way I can know to bring it up later. Is there anything like that going on here? If so, I'd love to hear about it. I'll just listen, without defending myself."
  "Are you feeling all right physically? Are you hurting anywhere? Or sick in any way?"

- Make specific offers.

  Sometimes I'm just too empty to tell you whether something is wrong, and I just need you to love me. That's the only thing that works. So if you just offer me some love, that would be great. I know that takes effort on your part—a completely one-way effort, so I especially appreciate it. I feel like a child on those occasions, in fact. Here are some things you could do or say:

  > Ask me if I want something cold to drink, or just bring me something to drink and set it there next to me.

  > Sit next to me and just say nothing for a while. Don't be in a hurry. Then start at the top of the list of general questions again.

  > Sit next to me and touch me on the leg. Tell me you're not in a hurry to leave. Tell me that you'd love to hear whatever I want to talk about. Then just sit and wait for a few more minutes. If I don't talk, then tell me you're leaving, but you'll be back in ten minutes to ask if I want anything.

- Leave him alone.

  Sometimes I'm just too empty and cranky for any approach to work. On those occasions you might have to just give up, or I might be able to tell you to just leave me alone for a while, to save you the trouble of going through all the steps. On those occasions, leave me alone, but then come back in twenty minutes or so and ask me if I feel any different and if I want to talk.

You'll be sharing this assignment with your partner tomorrow, on Day Twenty-Nine.

DAY THIRTY:
The Primary Decision and More

First Assignment

Share your Fourth Assignment from Day Twenty-Nine with your partner. You are both sharing valuable information here with your partner about your condition when you're empty and afraid. Work out the four-step approach in detail with your partner, and write down the results. You will find that this information is as valuable as gold when either of you is in a condition of angry withdrawal.

Second Assignment

In the meeting, read from the book *Real Love in Marriage*:
Begin   Page 160, Title: Making the Primary Decision . . .
End   Page 169, Title: Exercises

(Complete the following assignments outside the meeting.)

Third Assignment

I have seen few influences or decisions make a more powerful difference in a marriage than a willingness on the part of *either* partner to make the Primary Decision. Once you have chosen to make your partner the most important person in your life, a great many other decisions become much easier—even simple—and many conflicts simply disappear.

In the following space describe how making the Primary Decision might affect some of the issues in your marriage. Pages 160-165 of *Real Love in Marriage* will give you some guidelines—and examples— for completion of this assignment, and I will offer a couple more examples here:

- My wife has been telling me for a long time that I put my work ahead of her all the time. She says I'm always too busy, I put work projects before everything else, and so on. We have fights on subjects like this all the time. If I would make the Primary Decision, though, and put her first on a consistent basis, we wouldn't be having these fights. I realize that occasionally I might have to put work ahead of the things she wants, but overall the Primary Decision will bring us a lot of peace and happiness.

- For years I've been nagging my husband to pick up after himself, and he's really come to resent it—and it's become a real obstacle between us. If I make the Primary Decision, Larry would be the most important person in my life, more important to me than my own momentary convenience, and the conflict would stop. Sure, if I nag Larry enough I can get him to clean up a little more, but look at the cost: I make him unhappy, and I'm not happy either. And the reward for my nagging is so tiny, except that my pride is satisfied a little. I think the Primary Decision would be wiser. If Larry could see that I care about him, I believe we could have some reasonable conversations about a lot of things, including housekeeping.

You'll be sharing this assignment with your partner tomorrow, on Day Thirty-One.

Fourth Assignment

Recognize that when you are affected by some of the factors listed at the top of page 168 of *Real Love in Marriage* you will be far less able to participate in loving interactions with anyone, including your partner. It may be wise, therefore, if you are affected by such factors, to notify your partner that you are handicapped, so that adjustments in your interactions can be made. In the following space describe how you might describe these circumstances and adjustments to your partner.

   Allow me to provide some examples of fulfilling this assignment, as though you were speaking to your partner:

- When I'm not feeling well—when I'm tired or sick or in a bad mood or for any reason not capable of being loving toward you—instead of surprising you by biting your head off, I'm going to try to let you know about how I'm feeling ahead of time. So let me try this: When I'm feeling bad, let me say, "I'm not feeling very well. That has nothing to do with you, and I don't want to take it out on you, so for a while I'm suggesting that you not involve me in any conversation that matters to you. I suggest that you not talk to me much for the next XX hours (or until I let you know that I'm feeling better).
- You know how grouchy I am around bedtime. I just don't do well when I'm tired, so I suggest that we not have any important discussion—or any discussion where there is a possibility of conflict—that takes place later than nine o'clock.

- You know how many conversations have gone badly when we've talked in the morning, because I'm not a morning person. So I suggest that we just not have important discussions in the morning. Would that be all right with you?
- If I'm not feeling very well—for any reason, emotional, physical, or whatever—I'm just going to tell you that it's not a good time for me to be having a conversation with you. And I'll *try* to give you an idea how long that will last, but you might have to check in on me to ask me if I'm doing better in a few hours.

You'll be sharing this assignment with your partner tomorrow, on Day Thirty-One.

Fifth Assignment

Share your Assignment with a wise friend, and in the space below describe this experience.

Sixth Assignment

In the Fourth Assignment of Day Twenty-One, you committed to find your partner and indicate some measure of unsolicited affection at least four times a week, and to calendar this activity, probably using the same calendar as for the Sixth Assignment of Day Twenty. In the space below, describe the results of this effort. Are you keeping your commitment? As a result of your loving acts, are you feeling an increased connection with your partner? Are you feeling happier yourself? Are you seeing any change in your relationship?

DAY THIRTY-ONE:
The Unique Commitment of Marriage

First Assignment

Share your Third Assignment from Day Thirty with your partner. As you commit to the Primary Decision together, this can be a very bonding experience for you.

Second Assignment

Share the Fourth Assignment from Day Thirty with your partner. You are sharing valuable information here with your partner about your emptiness and fear. You will find this very useful in the future.

Third Assignment

In the meeting, read from the book *Real Love in Marriage*:
Begin   Page 171, Title: The Unique Union
End   Page 180, Title: The Power of Faith

(Complete the following assignments outside the meeting.)

Fourth Assignment

In the following space describe some of the expectations you have heaped on your partner, expectations that you now believe may have contributed to the disappointment and conflict in your relationship. Allow me to provide some possible examples:

I have expected my partner to
- maintain the same level of excitement he did when we were dating.
- keep me from ever feeling alone.
- always make me feel safe.
- always be emotionally stable, to never be angry or upset at me.
- provide the same level of sexual attraction and excitement as when I first met her.
- provide perfect financial security for me.
- make me happy all the time.
- make up for all the emptiness and unhappiness that I've known all my life.

You'll be sharing this assignment with your partner tomorrow, on Day Thirty-Two.

Fifth Assignment

Relationships are most successful when one or, preferably, both parties are willing to love unconditionally, when they are willing to contribute to the welfare of the other without thought for what they will get in return. This one-sided loving is essential to joyful relationships but is contrary to what is generally seen in the world, where the rule is score-keeping and trading and meticulous accounting.

In the space below describe an occasion when you gave of yourself to your partner in a one-sided way: where you gave your time, attention, effort, forgiveness, or something—your love—without getting anything in return. Describe how it felt. Did you feel more connected to your partner? Did you feel less alone? Did you feel happier?

If this was a positive experience, you might consider repeating such acts on a regular basis, some of which we discussed in assignments for Days Eighteen through Twenty (especially Day Twenty).

You will not be sharing this assignment with your partner, because there is a tendency to tell such stories in order to receive gratitude, which is not compatible with your present motivation to act with unconditional motives toward your partner.

Sixth Assignment

Share your Assignment with a wise friend, and in the space below describe this experience.

DAY THIRTY-TWO:
Faith and Unity

First Assignment

Share the Fourth Assignment from Day Thirty-One with your partner. Your partner can often experience an enormous relief as he or she hears you talk about the unreasonable expectations you have heaped upon him or her for so long. These can be a huge emotional burden. Of course it will be helpful if you acknowledge that these expectations have been unreasonable on your part. You can experience a similar relief as you hear your partner talk about his or her expectations.

Second Assignment

In the meeting, read *aloud* from the book *Real Love in Marriage*:
Begin   Page 180, Title: The Power of Faith
End   Page 187, Title: Exercise

Third Assignment (in the meeting)

All the principles in this book are worthless without faith, as defined at the top of page 181 of *Real Love in Marriage*. Until we make a decision to simply trust in what we cannot yet fully understand, and take steps to move forward in the direction of new principles, our lives cannot possibly change in a positive direction.

Toward that end, read the following to your partner in the meeting:

- I choose to have faith rather than doubt.
- I choose to have faith that Real Love will be more effective in our relationship than anger and fear and all the Getting and Protecting Behaviors have been.

- I choose to have faith in telling the truth about myself instead of hiding and lying and staying alone.
- I choose to have faith that you are doing the best you can to learn to be loving, instead of doubting you and criticizing you and believing that somehow you are intentionally holding back and trying to fail.
- I have faith that being one with you—being a partner with you—will be more beautiful and will be a happier experience than being separate from you and attacking you and not loving you.

Now allow your partner to read the above to you.

- How does it feel to say these things?
- How does it feel to hear them?
- Are you willing to allow the power of faith to transform your life? If so, repeat the above phrases to each other at regular intervals in your daily couple's meetings.

If you are completing this workbook alone, simply imagine reading this to your partner, which can still have a very positive effect.

(Complete the following assignment outside the meeting.)

Fourth Assignment

In the Fifth and Sixth Assignments of Day Twenty, you committed to create a list of loving acts, at least one of which you would demonstrate toward your partner. You also committed to calendar these acts. In the following space, describe the results of this effort. Are you keeping your commitment? As a result of your loving acts, are you feeling an increased connection with your partner? Are you feeling happier yourself? Are you seeing any change in your relationship? (Keep in mind, however, that you don't want to initiate any "loving act" *so that* your partner will react in any particular way, or your motivation wouldn't be *unconditional*.)

DAY THIRTY-THREE:
Making Requests

First Assignment

In the meeting, read from the book *Real Love in Marriage*:
Begin   Page 188, Title: Making it Work
End   Page 197, Title: Make Requests Clear and Specific

(Complete the following assignments outside the meeting.)

Second Assignment

Part of the process of two people working and being together as a couple is their bringing into the relationship their combined talents and efforts. For optimum effectiveness, this requires that each person make regular requests of the other partner, in order to make the most productive use of both partners' time and abilities. If we make these requests with a genuine concern for our partner, a beautiful synergy can be achieved, a harmony that most people can scarcely imagine. If these "requests" are made without this requisite concern, however, they can introduce and nourish malignant seeds that can end relationships.

The pages listed above describe many of the characteristics to be avoided when making genuine requests, but we can make it all much easier to remember by summarizing the features of demands as follows: manipulation or intimidation beforehand and irritation afterward. If you do anything at all to manipulate your partner to get what you want as you are "requesting" it, you are not making a true request. You're just making a clever demand. And if you don't get what you "request," and you feel *any* irritation, you were also not making a request.

In the space below describe some requests you've made that have interfered with the Real Love in your relationship. Allow me to offer some examples of this assignment:

- All these years I thought I'd been *asking* my husband to pick up his clothes and be more neat around the house. But I wasn't *asking* him to do anything. Almost every time I brought up the subject, I was angry, and whenever he didn't respond as I wanted, I was angry again. I've been very unloving.
- For a long time I've been complaining about my asking for more sex and not getting it. The truth is, I've been manipulating her for it, pushing her for her, intimidating her for it, and then when I didn't get it, I got angry. There was no real asking and no loving. I've been doing it all wrong. No wonder she didn't want to have sex with me.
- I've been nagging him to spend more time with my family, and then when he hasn't, I've been badmouthing him to my family and criticizing him for not being a good husband. I've turned it into a really negative issue. He's reacted by wanting to be around me even less, whether my family is involved or not. I've just made everything worse by pushing my demand.

You'll be sharing this assignment with your partner tomorrow, on Day Thirty-Four.

Third Assignment

Share your Second Assignment with a wise friend, and in the space below describe this experience.

DAY THIRTY-FOUR:
Clear and Specific Requests

First Assignment

Review the Second Assignment from Day Thirty-Three with your partner. It can be such a relief for your partner to hear the truth about something that has been a cause of tension for a long time. Simply telling the truth about these things can eliminate much confusion, along with the pain.

Second Assignment

In the meeting, read from the book *Real Love in Marriage*:
Begin   Page 197, Title: Make Requests Clear and Specific
End   Page 203, Title: Listen and Accept

(Complete the following assignments outside the meeting.)

Third Assignment

Following the pattern described and examples provided in the pages listed above, use the following space to write some specific requests that you'd like to make of your partner:

You'll be sharing this assignment with your partner tomorrow, on Day Thirty-Five.

Fourth Assignment

Share your Assignment with a wise friend, and in the space below describe this experience. He or she may also have some advice to give about the requests you have come up with.

Fifth Assignment

In the Fifth Assignment of Day Twenty-One, you made a commitment that you would let go of a resentment that you held toward your partner, using the tools described in that assignment. How are you doing with that assignment? Have you managed to let go of that resentment completely? If not, are you continuing to work on it? Are you willing to? If you have let go of the resentment, how does it feel? Can you feel the increase in the power of Real Love between you as you have removed this obstacle? Are you willing to choose another resentment and let it go?

DAY THIRTY-FIVE:
Bringing Your Requests Together

First Assignment

In the meeting, read from the book *Real Love in Marriage*:
Begin   Page 203, Title: Listen and Accept
End   Page 210, Title: Agreements and Expectations

Second Assignment (still in the meeting)

Choose a request from your Third Assignment of Day Thirty-Four. Present it to your partner as a genuine request, using all the principles governing requests that were presented in the *Marriage* book:

- Realize that Real Love is always the most important thing
- Ask, don't demand
- Make requests clear and specific
- Listen and accept
- Modify your requests where necessary

If you have difficulty with a request—in other words, if Getting and Protecting Behaviors arise—go back to the above principles, especially remembering that Real Love is the most important thing. If necessary, drop the request and try another one. You'll also be able to address these requests in future couple's meetings for months and years to come.

(Complete the following assignments outside the meeting.)

Third Assignment

In the following space, discuss what you learned from completing the Second Assignment above with your partner. As you made your request, what did you observe about your fears? Your tendency to manipulate and control? Your Getting and Protecting Behaviors?

You'll be sharing this assignment with your partner tomorrow, on Day Thirty-Six.

Fourth Assignment

Share your Assignment with a wise friend, and in the space below describe this experience.

DAY THIRTY-SIX:
Agreements and Expectations

First Assignment

Share the Third Assignment from Day Thirty-Five with your partner. It can be fun and quite endearing for our partners to hear what we have learned from our experiences with them, even—and sometimes especially—when those experiences were difficult.

Second Assignment

In the meeting, read from the book *Real Love in Marriage*:
Begin   Page 210, Title: Agreements and Expectations
End   Page 217, bottom of page

(Complete the following assignments outside the meeting.)

Third Assignment

In the following space, choose a task or subject about which you would like to create an agreement between you and your partner. Using the suggestions in the pages above, create the desired agreement.

You'll be sharing this assignment with your partner tomorrow, on Day Thirty-Seven.

Fourth Assignment

Share your Third Assignment with a wise friend, and in the space below describe this experience. He or she may also have suggestions that will prove useful as you talk with your partner.

Fifth Assignment

In the Fifth and Sixth Assignments of Day Twenty, you committed to create a list of loving acts, at least one of which you would demonstrate toward your partner. You also committed to calendar these acts. In the space below, describe the results of this effort. Are you keeping your commitment? As a result of your loving acts, are you feeling an increased connection with your partner? Are you feeling happier yourself? Are you seeing any change in your relationship? (Keep in mind, however, that you don't want to initiate any "loving act" *so that* your partner will react in any particular way, or your motivation wouldn't be *unconditional*.)

DAY THIRTY-SEVEN:
Meddling in the Business of Our Partners

First Assignment

Share the Third Assignment from Day Thirty-Six with your partner. This can sometimes be a difficult assignment. If you are not completely successful, set the assignment aside and try again another day. Do not persist if Getting and Protecting Behaviors arise.

Second Assignment

In the meeting, read from the book *Real Love in Marriage*:
Begin   Page 220, Title: Into the Lion's Mouth
End   Page 226, Title: When *Not* to Tell Your Partner the Truth

(Complete the following assignments outside the meeting.)

Third Assignment

When we are wise and loving, we remember the Law of Choice and mostly stay out of our partners' business. We do not point out their mistakes. We realize that dealing with our own flaws is more than enough to occupy our time and effort. There are occasions, however, when our partners could actually benefit from our describing their mistakes, when we could (1) create opportunities for them to feel loved and (2) allow them to see choices that would be more beneficial to them. Regrettably, we often do not point out the mistakes of our partners for those two reasons but rather because their mistakes simply inconveniences us or, worse, because we selfishly enjoy the sense of power we get from highlighting their flaws.

If you are thinking of mentioning one of your partner's mistakes or flaws, therefore, first be certain that the primary benefit is to your partner, not you. But that is not enough. The conditions of your speaking must also be correct, or the message cannot be received. You must deliver the message in a loving way, *and* your spouse must be in a position to actually *hear* what you will say. If he or she is sufficiently empty and afraid, he won't be *able* to hear you, and then your speaking can only be unproductive.

In the following space, name a mistake or flaw that you have tried to communicate to your partner, and describe why it has been your fault that the communication has been unsuccessful. Allow me to provide a couple of examples:

- For years I've told my wife that she buys way more clothes than she needs. I make excuses for my criticism, telling her that she's just trying to get people to like her, and that she needs to get over that. Well, maybe that's true, but when I talk to her about it, I'm far from loving, so there's no way she can hear what I'm saying. She needs my unconditional love in a hundred ways a lot more than she needs my criticism on this one subject. When I talk about it, all she hears me say is, "I don't love you."
- I tell my husband that he watches television too much, and that he'd be happier if he got off the couch and did other things, like exercise. He needs to lose some weight too. It would be good for him. But I'm just using that "good for him" excuse as a way to get him to do what I want. It really just bothers *me* that he watches television and doesn't do as much with me as he used to. And I'm worried that he's going to get fat and unhealthy. And when I talk to him about it, I'm quite unloving, so there's no way he can hear a word I'm saying.

You'll be sharing this assignment with your partner tomorrow, on Day Thirty-Eight.

Fourth Assignment

Share your Assignment with a wise friend, and in the space below describe this experience.

DAY THIRTY-EIGHT:
When Not to Meddle

First Assignment

Share the Third Assignment from Day Thirty-Seven with your partner. As your partner shares his or her assignment with you, just be grateful that he or she is willing to share these communication mistakes with you. This is an opportunity for your partner to be open and vulnerable with you. Don't ruin this by rubbing it in with too many comments of your own.

Second Assignment

In the meeting, read from the book *Real Love in Marriage*:
Begin   Page 226, Title: When *Not* to Tell Your Partner the Truth
End   Page 231, Title: How to Tell Your Spouse the Truth . . .

(Complete the following assignments outside the meeting.)

Third Assignment

In the following space, describe a specific occasion when you pointed out a mistake or flaw in your partner when the interaction went poorly. In light of your reading above—and what you know of Real Love—discuss why that interaction went badly. This is somewhat similar to the Third Assignment of Day Thirty-Seven, except you have learned the additional principles of pages 226-231 above to guide your answer. Allow me to provide some abbreviated examples:

- My husband was yelling at our son, Jesse, and I came in from the other room and told him that he needed to calm down. I realize now that nobody likes to be corrected while they're in the middle of making a mistake, and they're especially unable to hear correction while they're empty and afraid—which he obviously was if he was angry. I could have handled that better.

- Yesterday Cheryl was trying to tell me that I had run one of the credit cards over the limit, but instead of listening I said I couldn't talk to her while she was being *like that*. Then she blew up even worse. When she's angry, what she needs is my love, not my pointing out that she's doing something wrong. I was wrong to do that.

- Two days ago Mike was walking out the door to meet with some friends of ours, and I said, "Are you going to wear that shirt?" He immediately became defensive, so I became defensive right back. But I was wrong. I forgot the four guiding questions from the *Real Love in Marriage Book* (pages 153-154) that will help prevent unnecessary conflict like that. In this case the guiding question was, "Is this any of my business?" It was none of my business to ask him about what he was wearing. I shouldn't have said anything.

- The other day Donna was driving, and I made a comment about how she could switch lanes and avoid a long line ahead. She didn't like my suggestion, and I was offended at her attitude. I thought I was just trying to "help." Now I see that even though my suggestion might have saved a little bit of time, frankly it just didn't matter that much, and it certainly wasn't worth criticizing her for such a small thing. I should have just shut up and let her do the driving.

You'll be sharing this assignment with your partner tomorrow, on Day Thirty-Nine.

Fourth Assignment

Share your Assignment with a wise friend, and in the space below describe this experience.

Fifth Assignment

In the Fourth Assignment of Day Twenty-One, you committed to find your partner and indicate some measure of unsolicited affection at least four times a week, and to calendar this activity, probably using the same calendar as for the Sixth Assignment of Day Twenty. In the space below, describe the results of this effort. Are you keeping your commitment? As a result of your loving acts, are you feeling an increased connection with your partner? Are you feeling happier yourself? Are you seeing any change in your relationship?

DAY THIRTY-NINE:
Suggestions and Listening

First Assignment

Share the Third Assignment from Day Thirty-Eight with your partner. As your partner shares his or her assignment with you, just be grateful that he or she is willing to share these communication mistakes with you. This is an opportunity for your partner to be open and vulnerable with you. Don't ruin this by rubbing it in with too many comments of your own.

Second Assignment

In the meeting, read from the book *Real Love in Marriage*:
Begin   Page 231, Title: How to Tell Your Spouse the Truth . . .
End   Page 238, Title: Exercise

(Complete the following assignments outside the meeting.)

Third Assignment

In light of all you have learned to this point, use the space below to describe how you will discuss with your partner one of his or her mistakes or flaws in a loving way.

You'll be sharing this assignment with your partner tomorrow, on Day Forty.

Fourth Assignment

Share your Third Assignment with a wise friend. He or she may have suggestions that will prove useful as you talk with your partner.

DAY FORTY:
Understanding the Problems in Sex

First Assignment

Share the Third Assignment from Day Thirty-Nine with your partner. As your partner shares his or her assignment with you, apply all the listening guidelines from pages 88-95, 116-120, and 237-238 of *Real Love in Marriage*. Genuine listening—especially while your partner is telling the truth about you—can be a very loving act on your part.

Second Assignment

In the meeting, read from the book *Real Love in Marriage*:
Begin   Page 240, Title: The Agony and the Ecstasy
End   Page 250, Title: The Physical Techniques of Great Sex

(Complete the following assignments outside the meeting.)

Third Assignment

In the following space describe how you have used sex as a form of Imitation Love in your life and in your marriage. How has that interfered with the happiness in your relationship? Make your statements as though you were addressing your partner. Allow me to provide some examples of this assignment:

- When I was an adolescent girl, I discovered the power of sex in attracting men into my life, and I used it from then on. I used it to attract you as a partner too, and I have used it on many occasions to manipulate you to get what I've wanted. So I've used sex to my advantage a lot, but on many occasions I get angry when you want sex. Considering how I've used sex to attract you and manipulate you, that would seem pretty confusing and inappropriate on my part, wouldn't it?

- I've been using women for sex from the time I was a boy—fantasies, porn, talking about sex, actually having sex, everything—just for my own pleasure. And I've used you. It's been really selfish on my part, and I'm sure it's made you feel unloved many times.

- Sometimes I refuse to have sex with you just because I know it bothers you. It gives me a sense of power over you. That's pretty ugly of me, but it's true.

- Sometimes I dress up to go out in public knowing that other men will be looking at me. When they look at me, I feel good.

- Since we've been married, sometimes I have used pornography, which must make you feel like I'm cheating on you. To be honest, it is a kind of cheating.

- Sometimes I flirt with other women, and in the past I've justified it as an innocent thing, but it's wrong. I do it to feel better about myself, and it's selfish.

- Sometimes when you get more enjoyment than I get from the sex we have, I feel irritated. If I really cared about your happiness, I wouldn't care about those times. I would just talk to you more and figure out a way that I could get more pleasure out of sex the next time, or more pleasure overall.

You'll be sharing this assignment with your partner tomorrow, on Day Forty-One.

Fourth Assignment

In the Fifth and Sixth Assignments of Day Twenty, you committed to create a list of loving acts, at least one of which you would demonstrate toward your partner. You also committed to calendar these acts. In the space below, describe the results of this effort. Are you keeping your commitment? As a result of your loving acts, are you feeling an increased connection with your partner? Are you feeling happier yourself? Are you seeing any change in your relationship? (Keep in mind, however, that you don't want to initiate any "loving act" *so that* your partner will react in any particular way, or your motivation wouldn't be *unconditional*.)

DAY FORTY-ONE:
Discussing Sex

First Assignment

Share the Third Assignment from Day Forty with your partner. Be kind and loving as your partner shares his or her faults with you.

Second Assignment

In the meeting, read from the book *Real Love in Marriage*:
Begin   Page 250, Title: The Physical Techniques of Great Sex
End   Page 268, Title: Resolving Conflicts about Sex
(This is an unusually long reading assignment. You may decide to finish it outside your meeting.)

(The following assignment to be completed outside the meeting)

Third Assignment

In the following space, describe some sexual activities that you would prefer to engage in more often with your partner, including variations in timing and foreplay. Make your statements as though you were addressing your partner. Allow me to provide just a few answers to this assignment:

- I would really like it if we had the daily couple's meetings, like we committed to have in the Sixth Assignment of Day Nineteen. When we talk on a regular basis, I feel much closer to you and much more like having sex
- I like it when you touch me several times every day in non-sexual ways. If you'll do that, I won't feel like you touch me only when you want sex.

- I would love it if you went with me to a bookstore and bought a book on sexual positions, and then if we tried out some of them.
- I would like to just go over your body from head to toe with the lights on, examining every inch of you, without you squirming to get away from me.
- For a while, I'd like you to make sure that I have an orgasm first, before you do, every time we have sex. Otherwise I tend not to get one. And I'd like to tell you how I'd like to get it.
- I want to have sex with you with the lights on. All of them.
- I'd like you to ask me for sex three times in a row. Within ten days. That makes me really feel wanted by you.
- The next several times I ask you if you're interested in sex, I'd like you to not pause or hesitate in the slightest but act completely thrilled when you say *yes*.

You'll be sharing this assignment with your partner tomorrow, on Day Forty-Two.

DAY FORTY-TWO:
Conflicts about Sex and Infidelity

First Assignment

Share the Third Assignment from Day Forty-One with your partner. As you do this, understand that you are not submitting an invoice for payment. These are *requests*. Remembering that, as your partner reads each of his or her requests, I suggest that you respond to each of them in one of the following ways:

- Accept. Say some variation on, "Yes, I'd be glad to." Then make some oral or written commitment as to when this will happen or begin.
- Modify. You may not be agreeable to that exact request, but you might be agreeable to something similar to it. You can read some examples of modifying a request on page 264 of *Real Love in Marriage*.
- Postpone. Say some variation on, "I don't think I'm ready to respond to that yet. Can we talk more about this later?" Then set up a date and time when you'll be ready to respond to this request.
- Deny. Just because your partner makes a request doesn't mean you have to agree to it. Say some variation on, "No, I couldn't do that."

Second Assignment

In the meeting, read from the book *Real Love in Marriage*:
Begin   Page 268, Title: Resolving Conflicts about Sex
End   Page 281, Title: Exercises

(The following assignment is to be completed outside the meeting.)

Third Assignment

In the space below, describe any conflicts that you and your partner are still having about sex.

You'll be sharing this assignment with your partner tomorrow, on Day Forty-Three.

DAY FORTY-THREE:
Bringing It All Together

First Assignment

Share the Third Assignment from Day Forty-Two with your partner. If you're still having sexual conflicts, use the principals you studied yesterday and throughout the book to help you resolve these conflicts. If you can't resolve these conflicts today, don't be in a hurry. You'll have many opportunities to address these.

Second Assignment

Review the tools that you will now use for the months and years to come, that will enable you to continue the progress you have made thus far during the 40 day Challenge. Among other things, I suggest that you

- recommit to meeting together every day to read, schedule time together, and tell the truth about yourselves, as discussed in the Sixth Assignment of Day Nineteen.
- continue your commitment—as made in the Fifth and Sixth Assignments of Day Twenty—to consciously display loving acts with each other. These go far in establishing a foundation of love in a relationship.
- regularly find your partner and express love and concern for no reason, as you began to do in the Fourth Assignment of Day Twenty-One.
- continue to root out all resentments that you might feel toward your partner—a project that you began in the Fifth Assignment of Day Twenty-One. No matter what your efforts toward loving can build, resentments can often quickly tear all that down.

- spend at least two uninterrupted hours together—on a "date"—every week, which we discussed on the Third Assignment of Day Twenty-Nine.
- consider reading aloud to each other the statements on faith, as found in the Third Assignment of Day Thirty-Two.

Marriage requires constant nourishment, but the rewards are infinitely worthwhile. Fortunately even the process of nourishment is endlessly enjoyable. Have fun with what you have learned!!